FIRST-FIXING CARPENTRY MANUAL

L. J. GORING, FIOC, LCG

Associate of The Chartered
Institute of Building

Lecturer in Wood Trades at
Hastings College of Arts and Technology

Drawings by the author

George Godwin   London and New York

George Godwin
an imprint of:
Longman Group Limited,
Longman House, Burnt Mill, Harlow, Essex CM20 2JE, England
Associated companies throughout the world.

Pubished in the United States of America
by Longman Inc., New York

© L. J. Goring 1983

First published 1983
Reprinted 1985

British Library Cataloguing in Publication Data

Goring, L. J.
    First-fixing carpentry manual.
    1. Carpentry
    I. Title
    694'.2   TH5604

    ISBN 0-7114-5795-6

Library of Congress Cataloging in Publication Data

Goring, L. J.
    First-fixing carpentry manual.

    Includes index.
    1. Carpentry — Handbooks, manuals, etc.
I. Title.
TH5608.G6   1983   694   82-17138
ISBN 0-7114-5795-6 (pbk.)

Produced by Longman Singapore Publishers (Pte) Ltd.
Printed in Singapore.

CONTENTS

To the Gorings and their offspring, especially Mary,
Penny, Jonathan and Jennifer

PREFACE

Without wishing to limit the readership of this book, it must be stated that it was written primarily for apprentices, trainees and building students, but should also be of interest to established tradespeople seeking to reinforce any weak or sketchy areas in their knowledge – especially with regard to such subjects as the chapter on interpretation of presentday stair regulations.

As a work of reference, it may also be of value to vocational teachers, lecturers and instructors – and finally, although not intentionally, the sequential, detailed treatment of the work should appeal to the keen DIY enthusiast.

Although many worthy books have been published dealing with carpentry and joinery, the approach has mainly been from a technical viewpoint with wide general coverage – and I believe that there is a certain need for books or manuals that deal with the sequence and techniques of performing the various, separate specialisms of the trade. Such is the aim of this book, to present a practical step-by-step progression through the first of these subjects, namely *first-fixing carpentry*.

This area of work is defined as meaning any carpentry – such as roofing and floor joisting – required to be done **before** plastering takes place; second fixing, therefore, being those tasks – such as skirting and architrave fixing – that take place **after** plastering. Most carpenters cover both areas of this work, although some specialize in either one or the other. Joinery, if only by definition of being manufactured in workshops, is a completely separate specialism.

Finally, it must be mentioned that not only do technical terms, methods and techniques vary in different parts of the country, but so also do the technical opinions of one person to another; controversy is generally rampant and it is wise to hear all, see all – and decide for yourself which is best.

L. J. Goring

LIST OF ABBREVIATIONS

bdg	boarding
bldg	building
BMA	bronze metal antique
c/c	centres
¢	centre line
cpd	cupboard
DPC	damp-proof course
DPM	damp-proof membrane
dia	diameter
ø	diameter
EML	expanded metal lathing
ex.	prefix to material size before being worked
f.f.l.	finished floor level
GL	ground level
hdb	hardboard
hwd	hardwood
ms	mild steel
NLT	not less than
NMT	not more than
p.a.r.	planed all round
PVA	polyvinyl acetate (adhesive)
r.h.w.	round-head wire (nails)
swd	softwood
T & G	tongued and grooved
TRADA	Timber Research and Development Association

TECHNICAL DATA

STANDARD TIMBER-SIZES

The following chart gives the British Standard sectional sizes of sawn softwood available to the industry – and it should be borne in mind that any non-standard requirement represents a special order and is likely to cost more.

Standard metric lengths are based on a 300 mm module, starting at 1.8 m and increasing by 0.3 m to 2.1 m, 2.4 m, 2.7 m and so on, up to 6.3 m. Non-standard lengths above this, usually from North American species, may be obtained up to about 7.2 m.

mm		75	100	125	150	175	200	225	250	300
	inches	3	4	5	6	7	8	9	10	12
16	⅝	√	√	√	√					
19	¾	√	√	√	√					
22	⅞	√	√	√	√					
25	1	√	√	√	√	√	√	√	√	√
32	1¼	√	√	√	√	√	√	√	√	√
38	1½	√	√	√	√	√	√	√		
44	1¾	√	√	√	√	√	√	√	√	√
50	2	√	√	√	√	√	√	√	√	√
63	2½		√	√	√	√	√	√		
75	3		√	√	√	√	√	√	√	√
100	4		√		√		√		√	√
150	6				√		√			√
200	8						√			
250	10								√	
300	12									√

STANDARD DOOR-SIZES

Door frames and linings may vary considerably in size, but are normally made to accommodate standard door sizes. Again, it must be realized that special doors, made to fit non-standard frames, considerably increase the cost of the job. The locations given to the groups of standard door-sizes below, are only a guide, not a fixed rule.

	Metric			Imperial		
	height (m)	width (mm)	thickness (mm)	height (ft/in)	width (ft/in)	thickness (in)
Main entrance doors	2.133	914	45	7 0	3 0	1¾
	2.032	813	45	6 8	2 8	1¾
	1.981	838	45	6 6	2 9	1¾
Room doors	1.981	762	45	6 6	2 6	1¾
	1.981	762	35	6 6	2 6	1⅜
Bathroom/ toilet doors	1.981	711	35	6 6	2 4	1⅜
	1.981	686	35	6 6	2 3	1⅜
	1.981	610	35	6 6	2 0	1⅜
Cupboard doors	1.981	533	35	6 6	1 9	1⅜
	1.981	457	35	6 6	1 6	1⅜
	1.828	610	35	6 0	2 0	1⅜

Note: When door frames and doors are required to be fire-resisting, special criteria laid down by the British Standards Institute must be adhered to – and a detailed reference to this is given in Chapter 6.

1 READING OF DRAWING NOTES

Technical drawings are necessary in most spheres of the building industry, as being the best means of conveying detailed and often complex information from the designer to all those concerned with the job. Building tradespeople, especially carpenters and joiners, should be familiar with the basic principles involved in reading drawings correctly. Mistakes on either side – in design or interpretation of the design – can be costly, as drawings form a legal part of the contract between architect/client and builder. This applies even on small jobs, where only goodwill may suffer; if a non-contractual drawing or sketch is supplied, it should be kept for a period of time after completion of the job, in case any queries should arise.

A simple sketch supplied by a client to a joinery shop for the production of a casement-type window is shown at **1a** .

The client's mistake in measuring between plastered reveals is illustrated at **1b** . Retention of the sketch protects the firm from the possibility of the client's wrongful accusation.

Another important rule is to study the whole drawing and be reasonably familiar with the details before starting work.

The following details are based on the guidelines laid down by the British Standards Institution, in their latest available publication entitled *Recommendations For Building Drawing Practice* (BS 1192 : 1969).

SCALES

Parts of metric scale rules, graduated in millimetres are shown at **2** . Each scale represents a ratio of given units (millimetres) to one unit (1 millimetre). Common scales are 1 : 100, 1 : 50, 1 : 20, 1 : 10, 1 : 5, and 1 : 1 (full size). For example, scale 1 : 5 = ⅕th full size, or 1 mm on drawing equals 5 mm in reality.

Although a scale rule is useful when reading drawings, because of the dimensional instability of paper preference should be given to written dimensions.

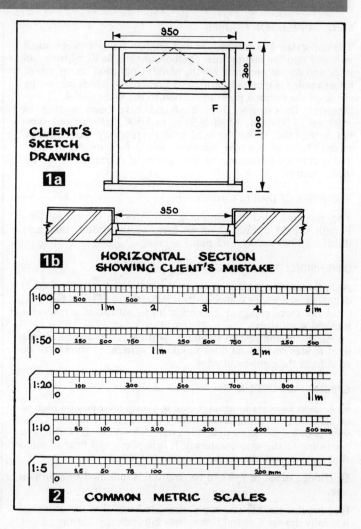

CLIENT'S SKETCH DRAWING **1a**

1b HORIZONTAL SECTION SHOWING CLIENT'S MISTAKE

2 COMMON METRIC SCALES

METRIC DIMENSION FIGURES

The abbreviated expression, or unit symbol, for metres is a small 'm', and mm for millimetres. Symbols are not finalized by a full stop, and do not use an 's' for the plural. Confusion occurs when, for example, $3\frac{1}{2}$ metres is written as 3.500 mm – which means, by virtue of the decimal point in relation to the unit symbol, $3\frac{1}{2}$ millimetres! To express $3\frac{1}{2}$ m, it should have been written as 3500 mm, 3 500 mm, 3.5 m, 3.50 m, or 3.500 m. Either one symbol or the other should be used on drawings: they should not be mixed. Normally, whole numbers should indicate millimetres, and decimalized numbers, to *three* places of decimals, should indicate metres.

SEQUENCE OF DIMENSIONING

The recommended dimensioning sequence is shown at **3**. Length should always be given first, width second, thickness third; e.g. $900 \times 200 \times 25$ mm.

DIMENSION LINES AND FIGURES

A dimension line with open arrows for basic/modular (unfinished) distances, spaces, or components is indicated at **4a** and **4b** indicates the more common dimension lines, with solid arrows, for finished work sizes.

All dimension figures should be written above and along the line; figures on vertical lines should be written, as shown, to be read from the right-hand edge.

SPECIAL-PURPOSE LINES

5 Section lines are imaginary cutting planes indicated on plan or in elevation, at a particular point to be exposed to view. The view is called the section, and is lettered A–A, B–B, and so on, according to the amount shown. It is important to bear in mind that the arrows indicate the direction of view.

6 Hidden detail or work to be removed is indicated by a broken line.

End break-lines **7a** (zig-zag pattern) indicate that the object is not fully drawn. Central break-lines **7b** indicate that the object is not drawn to scale in length.

8 Centre lines are indicated by a thin dot, dash chain.

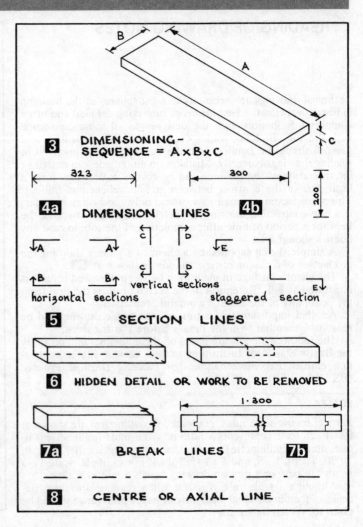

ORTHOGRAPHIC PROJECTION

Orthography is a Latin/Greek-derived word meaning *correct spelling* or *writing*. In technical drawing it is used to mean *correct drawing*; orthographic projection, therefore, refers to a conventional drawing method used to display the three-dimensional views (length, width, and height) of objects or arrangements as they will be seen on one plane – namely the drawing surface.

The recommended methods are known as *first-angle* (or European) *projection*, for building drawings, and *third-angle* (or American) *projection*, for engineering drawings.

First-angle projection

A box at **9a** is used as a means of explaining first-angle projection (f.a.p.). If you can imagine the object shown at **9b** to be suspended in the box, with enough room left for you to walk around it, then by looking squarely at the object on all sides, and from above, the views seen would be the ones shown on the surfaces in the background.

At **9c** the box is opened out to give the views as you saw them in the box, and as they should be laid out on a drawing. **9d** shows the symbol recommended for display on drawings to indicate that first-angle projection (f.a.p.) has been used.

Note: When views are separated onto different drawings, becoming unrelated orthographically, descriptive captions should be used such as *plan, elevation, etc.*

Third-angle projection

This is shown at **9e** for comparison only. This time the box has a top instead of a bottom; the views from the front and rear would be shown on the surface in the background, as before – but the views seen on the sides would be turned around and seen on the surfaces in the foreground; and the view from above (plan) would be turned and seen on the surface above. **9f** shows the symbol for third-angle projection.

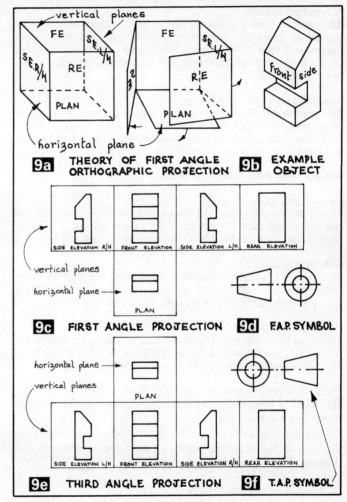

9a THEORY OF FIRST ANGLE ORTHOGRAPHIC PROJECTION

9b EXAMPLE OBJECT

9c FIRST ANGLE PROJECTION

9d F.A.P. SYMBOL

9e THIRD ANGLE PROJECTION

9f T.A.P. SYMBOL

Pictorial projections

10 Another form of orthographic projection produces what is known as pictorial projections, which preserve the three-dimensional view of the object. Such views have a limited value for working drawings, but serve well to illustrate technical notes and explanations.

Isometric projection

This is probably the most popular pictorial projection used, because of the balanced, 3-d effect. Shown at (a) consisting of vertical lines, and horizontal lines drawn at 30°. The length, width, and height, are to scale, expressed as ratio = 1 : 1 : 1.

Oblique projections – three variations

Cavalier projection

Shown at (b) with front (F) drawn true to shape, and side (S) elevations and plan (P) drawn at 45°, to a ratio of 1 : 1 : 1. Drawn true to scale, the object tends to look mis-shapen.

Cabinet projection

Shown at (c), similar to cavalier, except that the side and plan projections are only drawn to half scale, i.e. to a Ratio of 1 : 1 : $\frac{1}{2}$, making the object look more natural.

Planometric projection

Shown at (d), with plan (P) drawn true to shape, instead of the front view. Comprising verticals, and lines on front and sides at 45°. Often wrongly referred to as axonometric.

Perspective projections

11 Parallel perspective (a) refers to objects that diminish in depth to a vanishing point.

Angular perspective (b) refers to an object whose elevations diminish to two vanishing points. Of no value in pure technical drawing.

GRAPHICAL REPRESENTATION

12 This shows a selection of graphical symbols and representations used on building drawings.

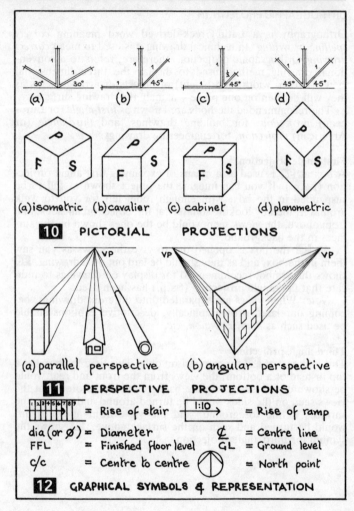

(a) isometric (b) cavalier (c) cabinet (d) planometric

10 PICTORIAL PROJECTIONS

(a) parallel perspective (b) angular perspective

11 PERSPECTIVE PROJECTIONS

= Rise of stair   1:10 = Rise of ramp
dia (or ø) = Diameter   ₵ = Centre line
FFL = Finished floor level   GL = Ground level
c/c = Centre to centre   = North point

12 GRAPHICAL SYMBOLS & REPRESENTATION

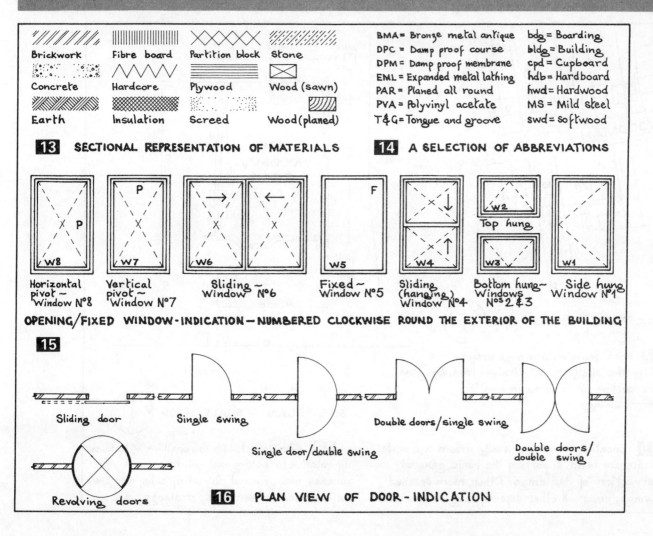

Brickwork | **Fibre board** | **Partition block** | **Stone**

Concrete | **Hardcore** | **Plywood** | **Wood (sawn)**

Earth | **Insulation** | **Screed** | **Wood (planed)**

BMA = Bronze metal antique
DPC = Damp proof course
DPM = Damp proof membrane
EML = Expanded metal lathing
PAR = Planed all round
PVA = Polyvinyl acetate
T&G = Tongue and groove

bdg = Boarding
bldg = Building
cpd = Cupboard
hdb = Hardboard
hwd = Hardwood
MS = Mild steel
swd = Softwood

13 SECTIONAL REPRESENTATION OF MATERIALS

14 A SELECTION OF ABBREVIATIONS

Horizontal pivot ~ Window Nº8 | Vertical pivot ~ Window Nº7 | Sliding ~ Window Nº6 | Fixed ~ Window Nº5 | Sliding (hanging) Window Nº4 | Bottom hung ~ Windows Nºs 2 & 3 | Side hung Window Nº1

P — W8 | P — W7 | W6 | F — W5 | W4 | W2 — Top hung — W3 | W1

OPENING/FIXED WINDOW-INDICATION—NUMBERED CLOCKWISE ROUND THE EXTERIOR OF THE BUILDING

15

Sliding door | Single swing | Single door/double swing | Double doors/single swing | Double doors/double swing

Revolving doors

16 PLAN VIEW OF DOOR-INDICATION

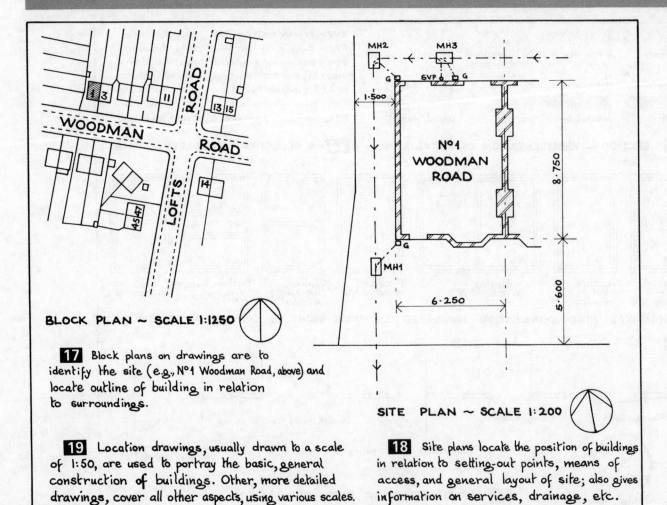

BLOCK PLAN ~ SCALE 1:1250

17 Block plans on drawings are to identify the site (e.g., N°1 Woodman Road, above) and locate outline of building in relation to surroundings.

19 Location drawings, usually drawn to a scale of 1:50, are used to portray the basic, general construction of buildings. Other, more detailed drawings, cover all other aspects, using various scales.

SITE PLAN ~ SCALE 1:200

18 Site plans locate the position of buildings in relation to setting-out points, means of access, and general layout of site; also gives information on services, drainage, etc.

2 FIRST-FIXING TOOLS: THEIR CARE AND PROPER USE

First-fixing carpentry is often wrongly referred to as 'rough carpentry, requiring little more than a hammer and saw'. In fact, the standard of workmanship should not be less than in any other carpentry job – and the tools required to cover the whole range of first-fixing operations are quite extensive, as the following details will indicate.

PENCILS

1 These must be kept sharp for accurate marking. Stumpy sharpening ⓐ should be avoided; sharpen to an angle of about 10° ⓑ. Use grade HB for soft, black lines on unplaned timber. Choose hexagon shape for better grip, and anti-roll action; and a bright colour to see easily when left lying amongst shavings, etc. Oval- or rectangular-shaped carpenters' pencils ⓒ of a soft or medium grade lead are better for heavy work such as roofing, joisting, etc., marking unplaned timber – although one disadvantage is that they cannot be put behind the ear for quick availability, as is the usual practice with ordinary pencils.

STEEL TAPE RULE

2 This is essential for fast, efficient measuring on site work. Models with lockable, retractable blades, 3.5 m long, are recommended. When retracting, slow down the last part of the blade to avoid damaging the metal hook at the end or nipping your fingers. To reduce the risk of kinking the sprung-steel blade, do not leave extended after use.

FOLDING RULE

3 One metre (1000 mm) unfolded length, 250 mm folded. Marked in millimetres, 5 mm, 10 mm (centimetres), and 100 mm (decimetres) graduations. Available in boxwood or tough, white Makrolon plastic with stainless steel ends and hinges. The latter rules are best for site work, but both should be folded after use to avoid hinge damage. Because of their thickness, to achieve

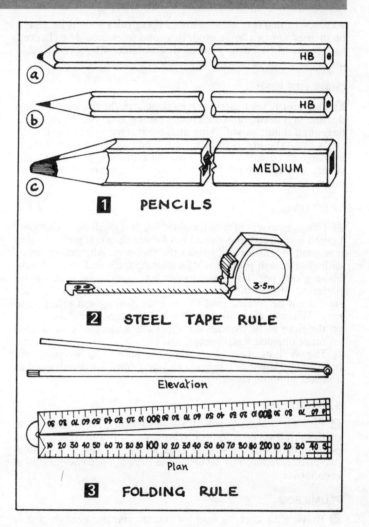

1 PENCILS

2 STEEL TAPE RULE

Elevation

Plan

3 FOLDING RULE

accuracy in marking or measuring, these rules should be rested on their edge when being used. Boxwood rules should be checked for length when being purchased, and later, after considerable use.

CHALK LINE REEL

4 This tool is very useful for marking straight lines by holding the line taut between two extremes, lifting at any mid point with finger and thumb, and flicking onto the surface to leave a straight chalk line. The line is retractable by winding. Powdered chalk is available in colours of red, white and blue. The reel has a subsidiary use as a plumb bob – but is not recommended for that purpose.

SPIRIT LEVEL

5 This is an essential tool for plumbing and levelling operations. Length is optional, but should not be less than 600 mm. 750 mm is a good length for fitting into the tool box. Aluminium levels with clear, tough plastic vials (containing spirit and trapped bubble) are very popular, or the conventional hardwood type may be preferred. Even though modern levels are shockproof, they should not be treated roughly, as body damage can effect accuracy. When resting the level between usages, avoid leaving it on the floor to be trodden on, especially when partly suspended on other objects, scrap timber, etc.

The skill of using your eyes for plumbing, levelling and measuring, should be practised and developed – but only used as a means of initial checking.

STRAIGHT EDGES

6 Parallel, straight boards of various lengths, for setting out or (with spirit level on top) for levelling, etc. If transferring a datum point in excess of the straight-edge length, the risk of a cumulative error is reduced by reversing the straight edge end-for-end at each move.

PLUMB BOB

7 Brass, mild steel, or lead, of various weights. Pear-shaped or cylindrical. Always suspend away from surface being checked, as indicated, and measure for equal readings at top and bottom. Wipe mild steel bobs with an oily rag occasionally.

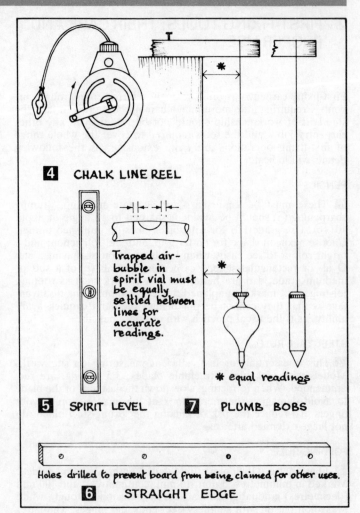

4 CHALK LINE REEL

Trapped air-bubble in spirit vial must be equally settled between lines for accurate readings.

5 SPIRIT LEVEL   **7** PLUMB BOBS

* equal readings

Holes drilled to prevent board from being claimed for other uses.

6 STRAIGHT EDGE

Although commonly called a plumb bob, if it is pointed on the underside, it is really a centre bob. The point is very useful for plumbing to a mark on the floor.

COMBINATION MITRE SQUARE

8 Adopted from the engineering trades and now widely favoured on site work for the following reasons: they are robust (the better types) and withstand normal site abuse; they can be used for testing or marking narrow rebated edges, as at (a), or to test or mark angles of 90°, 45° and 135°; the blade can be adjusted from the stock to a set measurement and, with the aid of a pencil, used as a pencil gauge. This is useful for marking sawn boards, for example, as opposed to using a marking gauge that may not be clearly visible on a rough sawn surface. The square's stock has an inset spirit vial, and can be used for plumbing and levelling – although this is not the tool's best feature. Always tighten the blade locking-nut after each adjustment, otherwise inaccuracies in the angle between the stock and blade will readily occur, causing errors in marking or testing. Finally, a scribing pin is often located in the end of the stock. This is a feature carried over from the square's originally intended use as an engineering tool, and is used for marking lines on metal.

SLIDING BEVEL

9 This is basically a slotted steel blade sliding and rotating from a hardwood stock. The blade is tightened by a screw or a half wing nut. The latter is best for ease and speed, being manually operated. An essential tool for angular work, roofing, etc. For protection, always return the blade to the stock-housing after use.

STEEL ROOFING SQUARE

10 Common size 600 × 450 mm (24 × 18 in.), marked with metric or imperial units. The long side is referred to as the *blade*, the short side as the *tongue*. This traditional tool is primarily for developing roofing bevels and lengths (covered in the chapter on roofing), but has a good subsidiary use as a 90° square, for marking and testing right angles on site.

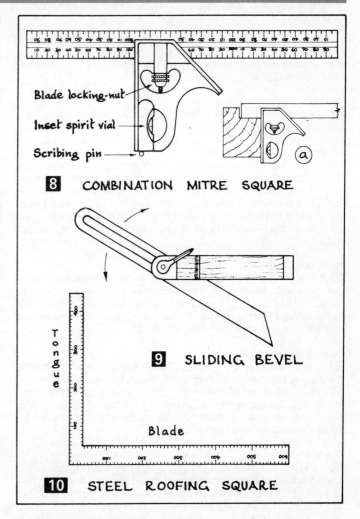

Blade locking-nut
Inset spirit vial
Scribing pin

8 COMBINATION MITRE SQUARE

9 SLIDING BEVEL

Tongue

Blade

10 STEEL ROOFING SQUARE

HANDSAWS

A selection of handsaws is advisable for first-fixing operations. These should include, in order of priority, a *crosscut saw, panel saw, general-purpose saw*, and, in the absence of a portable powered circular saw, a *rip saw*.

Crosscut saw

11 As the name implies, this is for cutting timber across the grain. Blade lengths and pp25 (points per 25 mm) or ppi (points per inch) vary, but 650 mm (26 in.) length and 7 or 8 pp25 are recommended. All handsaw teeth on conventional type saws contain 60° angular shapes, leaning, by varying degrees, towards the toe of the saw. The angle of lean, relative to the front cutting edge of the teeth, is called the *pitch*. When sharpening saws (covered in a separate chapter), it helps to know the required pitch. For crosscut saws the pitch should be 80°. When crosscutting, the saw – as shown – should be at an approximate angle of 45° to the timber.

Panel saw

12 A saw for fine crosscutting, which is particularly useful for cutting plywood, hardboard, etc. Recommendations are 550 mm (22 in.) blade length, 10 pp25 and 75° pitch. When cutting thin manufactured boards (plywood, hardboard, etc.), the saw should be used at a low angle of about 15° to 25°.

General-purpose saw

13 A saw with specially hardened teeth, which is used for cutting a variety of materials including wood, metal, laminates, chipboard, asbestos-cement or fibreboard sheets, etc. On the type illustrated, the handle can be adjusted to facilitate awkward in situ cuts; and the narrow width of the blade makes it useful for cutting certain curved shapes.

Rip saw

14 Used for cutting with the grain, this saw is rarely used nowadays because of the common use of machinery and portable power saws. However, it cannot be overlooked. Recommendations are 650 mm (26 in.) blade length, 5 or 6 pp25 and 87° pitch. When ripping (cutting with the grain), the saw should be used at a steep angle of about 60° to 70° to the timber.

All saws should be kept dry if possible, but if rusting does occur, soak liberally with oil and rub well with fine emery cloth.

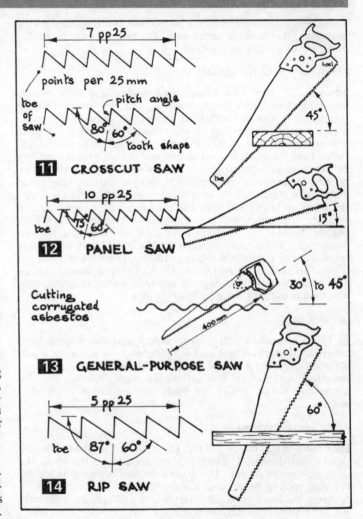

7 pp25

points per 25 mm

toe of saw

pitch angle

80° 60°

tooth shape

heel

45°

11 CROSSCUT SAW

10 pp25

toe

75° 60°

15°

12 PANEL SAW

Cutting corrugated asbestos

400 mm

30° to 45°

13 GENERAL-PURPOSE SAW

5 pp25

toe

87° 60°

60°

14 RIP SAW

CLAW HAMMER

15 Although this tool is basically for nailing and extracting nails, it has also been very widely used over the years, on its side, as an alternative to the wooden mallet. This is a reasonable practice on shatterproof-plastic chisel handles – especially as this type of handle is really too hard for the wooden mallet – but it is bad practice to use a hammer on wooden chisel handles, as they quickly deteriorate under such treatment. However, in certain awkward situations, the mallet is ineffective and one can only use the side of the claw hammer.

The claw is also used for a limited amount of leverage work, separating nailed boards, etc. To preserve the surface shape of the head, the hammer should not be used to chip or break concrete, brick or mortar, etc. When hammering normally, hold the lower end of the shaft and develop a swinging wrist action – avoid *throttling* the hammer (holding the neck of the shaft, just below the head). Choice of weights is between 450 g (1 lb) and 570 g (1½ lb); choice of type is between metal shaft, fibre shaft and conventional wooden shaft. The latter has a limited life-span on site work. The metal shafted type with shock-absorbent rubber grip, 570 g in weight, is recommended.

MALLET

16 The conventional wedge-shaped pattern, made of beech, is rather bulky and not favoured for site work, even though the tapered shaft – retaining the head from flying off – can be removed for easier carriage. A recommended alternative is a round-headed mallet, such as a Tinman's mallet – used normally by sheet-metal workers – which has a boxwood or lignum-vitae head of about 70 mm diameter. Finally, wooden mallets should only strike on their end grain – not on their sides.

SCREWDRIVERS

17 For first-fixing operations, where very little screwing is involved, a *cabinet* and a *ratchet* screwdriver should suffice. The recommended blade lengths are 200 and 100 mm respectively. For safety's sake, the blade-point of the screwdriver should be kept in its original good shape. Screwdrivers should not be used as levers, or hit with a hammer or a mallet.

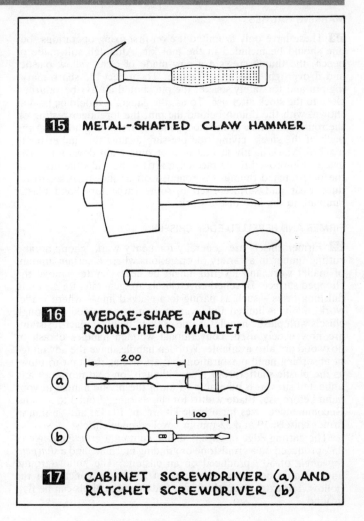

15 METAL-SHAFTED CLAW HAMMER

16 WEDGE-SHAPE AND ROUND-HEAD MALLET

200

ⓐ

100

ⓑ

17 CABINET SCREWDRIVER (a) AND RATCHET SCREWDRIVER (b)

MARKING GAUGES

18 These have only a limited use on first-fixing operations, but one should be included in the tool kit. Although still made of beech, the thumbscrews are now made of clear yellow plastic, and if overtightened, may fracture. To protect the sharp marking-pin and for safety's sake, the pin should always be returned close to the stock after use. To use the gauge, it should be held as shown, with the thumb behind the pin, the forefinger resting on the rounded surface of the stock, and the remaining fingers at the back of the stock, giving side pressure against the timber being marked. Mark lightly at first to overcome grain deviations. The gauge is improved if the face-edge arris – that rubs the inside of the outstretched thumb – is rounded off as shown. Also, to reduce wear and surface friction, some carpenters bond plastic laminate to the face of the stock.

FIRMER AND BEVELLED-EDGE CHISELS

19 Firmer chisels are generally for heavy work, chopping and cutting timber in a variety of operations where a certain amount of mallet work and levering might be necessary to remove the chopped surface. Bevelled-edge chisels are generally for accurate finishing tasks – such as paring to a gauged line – where mallet work, if any, is limited and levering should be avoided. Although chisels with plastic handles, some of them highly impact-resistant, are now widely used, conventional wooden handles of ash or boxwood are also available. Wooden handles have the advantage of absorbing hand-perspiration, but are not as resistant to blows as the plastic shatterproof type; although, on cold mornings and unheated sites, it is advisable to warm the plastic handle in your hand before use. Blade widths for chisels range from 3 to 51 mm. Recommended sizes for a basic kit are: 6, 10, 13, and 25 mm in firmer chisels; 19 and 32 mm in bevelled-edge chisels.

The cutting edge of chisels should contain a *grinding angle* of 25°, produced on a grindstone or grinding machine, and a *sharpening angle* of 30°, produced on an oilstone. The hollow-ground angle should not lessen the angle of 25° in the concave of the hollow. For extra strength, firmer and mortice chisels can be flat-ground.

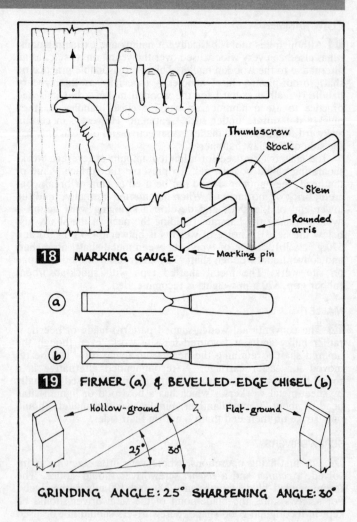

18 MARKING GAUGE

(a)

(b)

19 FIRMER (a) & BEVELLED-EDGE CHISEL (b)

GRINDING ANGLE: 25° SHARPENING ANGLE: 30°

OILSTONES

20 Artificially manufactured types, made from furnace-produced materials, as opposed to natural stone, are widely used because of their constant quality and relative cheapness. Coarse, medium and fine grades are available. A *combination stone*, measuring 200 × 50 × 25 mm, is recommended for site work. This stone is coarse for half its thickness, and fine on the alternate side for the remaining half thickness. As these stones are very brittle, they should be housed in purpose-made wooden boxes for protection. When sharpening, use a thin grade of oil, animal or mineral, but not vegetable oil, which tends to solidify on drying, so clogging the cut of the stone. Lubricating oil is very good.

Should the stone ever become clogged, giving a glazed appearance and a slippery surface, soak it in paraffin for several hours, then clean with a stiff brush or sacking material and allow to dry before re-using.

When sharpening chisels or plane irons, first apply enough oil to the stone to cover its surface and help float off the tiny discarded particles of metal, hold the tool comfortably with both hands, assume the correct angle to the stone (30°), and move back and forth in an even, unaltering movement until a small sharpened (or honed) edge is obtained. This action produces a metal burr which is turned back by reversing the cutter to lay flat on the stone, under finger-pressure, and rubbing up and down a few times. Any remaining burr can be removed by drawing the cutter across the arris edge of a piece of wood. The stone should always be used to its maximum length, the cutter lifted occasionally to bring the oil back into circulation. Narrow cutters, such as chisels, whilst traversing the length of the stone, should also be worked across the stone laterally to reduce the risk of dishing (hollowing) the stone in its width.

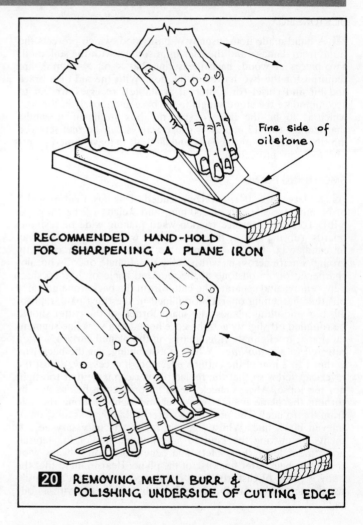

Fine side of oilstone

RECOMMENDED HAND-HOLD FOR SHARPENING A PLANE IRON

20 REMOVING METAL BURR & POLISHING UNDERSIDE OF CUTTING EDGE

OILSTONE BOX

21 A hand-made item, usually of hardwood, which protects the stone from damage and the user from contact with the soiled oil. Two pieces of wood, each measuring 240 × 62 × 18 mm, are required for the two halves of the box. With the aid of a brace and bit and chisel (or router, if available), recesses are cut to accommodate the stone snugly in the base and loosely in the part which is to be the lid. To stop the box from sliding whilst sharpening, two 12 mm × 4 gauge screws can be half-screwed into the underside of the base, and filed off to leave dulled points of 1 to 2 mm projection.

SMOOTHING PLANE

22 The large size, 04½, is recommended. This has a cutter width of 60 mm, base length of 260 mm, and weighs 2.2 kg (approx. 5 lb). To reduce surface friction when planing wide or resinous boards, rub the sole of the plane lightly with a piece of beeswax or candlewax. On new planes, the cutter has been correctly ground square across its width at the usual angle of 25° – but not sharpened on an oilstone at the required angle of 30°. To sharpen, remove and separate the cutter from the back iron and carry out the sharpening operation outlined in the third paragraph of **20**. For smoothing planes, the sharp corners of the cutter should be rounded off slightly and the edge honed to a very fine segmental shape, to eliminate ridge marks on the planed surface – often referred to as *tram lines*. When re-assembling, set the back iron within 1 to 2 mm of the cutter's edge and, if necessary, adjust the lever-cap screw so that the replaced lever cap is neither too tight nor too loose. Always check the cutter projection before use, by turning the plane over at eye-level and sighting along the sole from toe to heel. The projecting cutter will appear as an even or uneven black line. Whilst sighting, make any necessary adjustments by moving the knurled adjusting-nut and/or the lateral-adjustment lever. For safety and edge-protection, always wind the cutter back after final use of the plane. Bear in mind that the body is made of cast iron, and if dropped, is likely to fracture – usually across the mouth. Keep dry; rub occasionally with an oily rag.

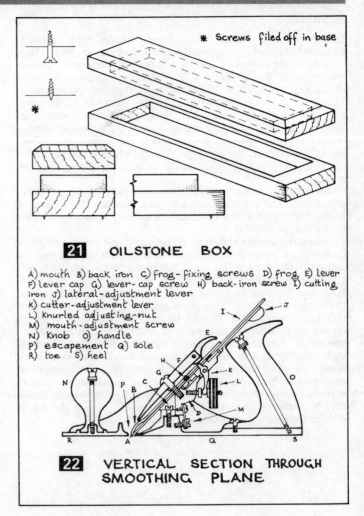

* Screws filed off in base

21 OILSTONE BOX

A) mouth B) back iron C) frog-fixing screws D) frog E) lever
F) lever cap G) lever-cap screw H) back-iron screw I) cutting
iron J) lateral-adjustment lever
K) cutter-adjustment lever
L) knurled adjusting-nut
M) mouth-adjustment screw
N) knob O) handle
P) escapement Q) sole
R) toe S) heel

22 VERTICAL SECTION THROUGH SMOOTHING PLANE

RATCHET BRACE

23 This item should be carefully chosen for its basic qualities, and any saving in cost could prove to be foolish economy. Essentially, the revolving parts – the head and the handle – should be free-running on ball bearings, the ratchet must be reliably operational for both directions, and the jaws must hold the tapered-tang twist bits, firmly and concentrically. Recommended *swing* (diameter of the handle's orbit) is 250 mm. Braces with a smaller or larger swing are available. The advantages of the ratchet are gained when drilling in situations where a full swing cannot be achieved, such as against a wall or in a corner – or when using the screwdriver bit under intense pressure and sustaining the intensity by using short, restricted ratchet-swings.

TWIST BITS

24 These are also referred to as *auger bits*, and are spiral-fluted, round shanked, with tapered tangs, and are generally for drilling deep holes from 6 to 38 mm diameter. *Jennings pattern* twist bits have a double spiral and are used for fine work; *Irwin solid-centre* twist bits have a single spiral and are more suitable for general-purpose work. Six bits, of the Irwin solid-centre pattern, are recommended for the basic kit, sizes 6, 10, 13, 16, 19, and 25 mm.

If the appearance of a hole has to be considered, then care must be taken not to break through on the other side of the timber being drilled. This is usually achieved by changing to the opposite side immediately the point of the bit appears. Alternatively, drill through into a piece of waste timber clamped onto or seated under the blind side.

Avoid sharpening twist bits for as long as possible, but when really necessary, sharpen the inside edges only, with a small file – never file the outer surface of the spur cutters. Take extra care when drilling fixed timbers, not to clash with concealed nails or screws, as this kind of damage usually ruins the twist bit.

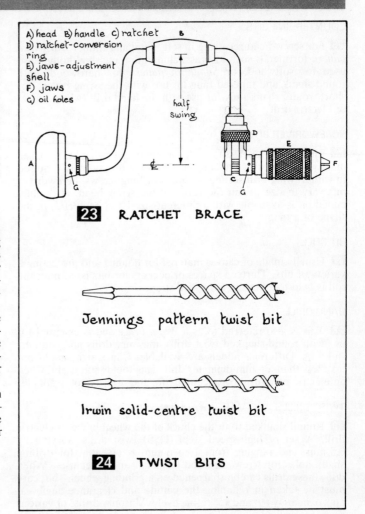

A) head B) handle C) ratchet
D) ratchet-conversion ring
E) jaws-adjustment shell
F) jaws
G) oil holes

half swing

23 RATCHET BRACE

Jennings pattern twist bit

Irwin solid-centre twist bit

24 TWIST BITS

COUNTERSINK BITS

25 For screw-head recessing in soft metal and timber. *Rosehead pattern* for metals such as brass, aluminium, etc. – although also used for softwood, or *Snailhorn pattern* for hardwood, with round shank and tapered tang for use with the swing brace – or short, round shank only for use with the hand drill (wheel brace) or electric drill.

SCREWDRIVER BITS

26 These have tapered tangs for use with the swing brace. Used mainly for the extra pressure and leverage occasionally required in withdrawing or inserting obstinate or long screws. Screwdriver bits vary in size to suit the gauge of the screw head. A double-ended bit is available with a different-size bit at each end, in the shape of a tang.

BIT ROLL

27 Usually made of canvas material for holding and protecting a variety of bits. Thirteen spaces or pockets for bits is normal; the roll is held together by a buckled strap.

HAND DRILL

28 This is also referred to as a *Wheel brace* and is essential for use with round-shanked twist drills, masonry drills and countersink bits. Different models are available. Chuck size should not take less than a 6 mm diameter drill. This tool is still useful when an electric hand-drill (or electricity for the drill) is not available.

TWIST DRILLS AND MASONRY DRILLS

29 Round-shanked to fit the chuck of the wheel brace or electric drill. A set of high-speed steel (HSS) twist drills, varying by 0.5 mm, and ranging from 1 to 6 mm, is essential for drilling shank holes for screws in wood or metal, and other uses. When dull, these drills can be sharpened on a grinding wheel – but care must be taken in retaining the cutting and clearance angles at approximately 60° and 15° respectively. Masonry drills, of various sizes, for drilling plug holes, etc. in brick, stone, concrete or similar materials, have tungsten carbide tips which, when dull, require sharpening on a special silicon carbide, green-grit grinding wheel. A 6 mm diameter masonry drill is a popular size to start with in the basic kit.

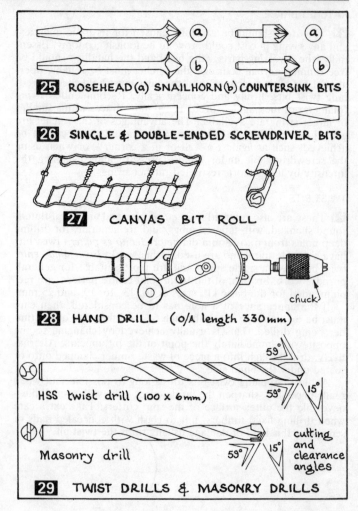

25 ROSEHEAD (a) SNAILHORN (b) COUNTERSINK BITS

26 SINGLE & DOUBLE-ENDED SCREWDRIVER BITS

27 CANVAS BIT ROLL

28 HAND DRILL (o/a length 330 mm)

HSS twist drill (100 × 6mm)

Masonry drill

cutting and clearance angles

29 TWIST DRILLS & MASONRY DRILLS

BRADAWLS

30 Used mainly for making small pilot holes when starting screw fixings. Different sizes are available. One type of awl has a flat brad-head point which should always be pushed into the timber at right angles to the grain; the other type of awl has a square-sectioned, tapered point which acts as a reamer when turned – ratchet fashion – into the timber. Although probably less common, the square-tapered awl is recommended.

CARPENTER'S AXE

31 Mostly used for rough reduction of waste wood from boards, and rough bevel-shaping, although traditionally also used for making propeller-shaped wooden plugs for wall fixings. The cutting edge can be sharpened either on a grinding machine or with a flat mill file to an angle of about 10° to 15° each side. Great care must be taken in using the axe safely; always keep the holding-hand at least 200 mm above and away from where the cutting edge is striking. When cutting small pieces of timber on end grain, use a *deadman's finger* for safety and accuracy, as illustrated, rather than risk holding the piece by hand near the point to be struck.

PINCERS

32 For withdrawing small nails and pins, not fully driven in. Although these are usually extracted by the claw hammer, occasionally a pair of pincers will do the job more successfully. When levering on finished surfaces, a small piece of wood or flat metal placed under the fulcrum point will reduce the risk of bruising the surface. Different sizes are available, but the 175 mm length is recommended.

WRECKING BAR

33 This tool is also referred to as *crowbar, nail bar* or *pinch bar*. Not essential, but useful for extracting large nails, and general leverage work. Choice of three sizes: 450, 600 and 750 mm. Leverage can be improved by placing various-size blocks under the fulcrum point.

HACKSAW

34 Another useful addition occasionally required. The *junior hacksaw*, with a 150 mm blade length, is recommended for the limited amount of use involved.

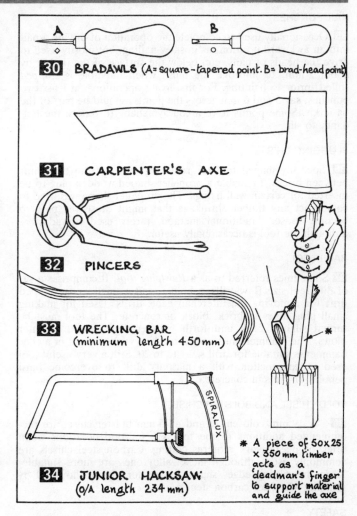

30 BRADAWLS (A = square-tapered point. B = brad-head point)

31 CARPENTER'S AXE

32 PINCERS

33 WRECKING BAR (minimum length 450mm)

34 JUNIOR HACKSAW (o/A length 234mm)

* A piece of 50 x 25 x 350 mm timber acts as a 'deadman's finger' to support material and guide the axe

NAIL PUNCHES

35 Occasionally used to complete the operation of driving a nail into an awkward position, as in skew-nailing, but mostly used to drive the heads of nails, etc. below the surface of the timber by about 2 mm, to improve the finish when the hole is *stopped* (filled) prior to painting. For first-fixing operations, at least two punches, say 3 and 6 mm across the points, should be part of the basic kit. Some points have a concave shape to reduce the tendancy to slip.

PLUGGING CHISEL

36 Specially-shaped tool for removing mortar from the joints between bricks, to enable a propeller-shaped wooden plug to be inserted for certain wall fixings. The propeller shape was used to counteract any timber shrinkage that might cause the plug to become loose. Traditional method, rarely used nowadays – although the tool is occasionally useful.

RAWLTOOL

37 Sometimes referred to as a *Rawlplug tool*. It comprises a set of different-size Rawldrills, a holder, and a small wedge-shaped drift for removing the interchangeable drills. Used for making small plug holes in brick, block or concrete. The tool must be turned slightly back and forth between light, rapid hammer blows. The hammer must not be too heavy; the weight of a claw hammer is suitable for drill sizes 12 to 20. Still a very useful tool used in conjunction with a masonry drill to overcome hard pebbles or flints in concrete.

COLD CHISEL AND BOLSTER CHISEL

38 A 19 mm cold chisel and a 75 mm bolster chisel are recommended additions to the tool kit, for odd occasions when brick or plasterwork requires cutting. Carbon steel chisels are commonly used, although nickel alloy ones are more suitable. Keep the cutting edges sharp, by file for nickel alloy and by grinding wheel for carbon steel.

SAFETY

35 to **38** For safety's sake, grind the sides of the heads before they become too mushroom-shaped from prolonged usage. Also, develop the technique of holding the tool as you would the barrel of a rifle, so that the palm of the hand, and not the knuckles, faces the hammer blows.

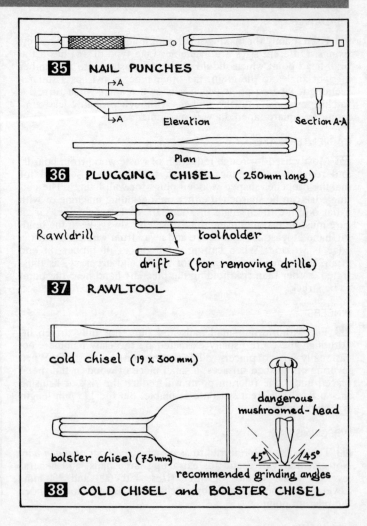

35 NAIL PUNCHES

Elevation   Section A-A

Plan

36 PLUGGING CHISEL (250mm long)

Rawldrill   toolholder

drift (for removing drills)

37 RAWLTOOL

cold chisel (19 x 300 mm)

dangerous mushroomed-head

bolster chisel (75mm)

recommended grinding angles

45° 45°

38 COLD CHISEL and BOLSTER CHISEL

PORTABLE POWERED CIRCULAR SAWS

39 These are often used nowadays to save time and energy spent on handsawing operations. Although basically for crosscutting and ripping, these saws can also be used for bevel cuts, sawn grooves and rebates. The purpose-built models with saw blades up to 240 mm diameter are recommended for site work.

Before use, the saw should be adjusted so that when cutting normally, the blade will only just break through the underside of the timber. This is easily achieved by releasing a locking device which controls the movement of the base plate in relation to the amount of blade exposed. For bevel cutting, the base tilts laterally through 45° on a lockable quadrant arm. The telescopic saw guard, covering the exposed blade, is under tension so that after being pushed back by the end of the timber being cut, it will automatically spring back when the cut is complete. For ripping, a detachable fence is supplied.

Before starting to cut, the saw should be allowed to reach maximum speed, and should not be stopped or restarted in the cut. Timber being cut should be securely held, clamped or fixed – making certain that any fixings will not coincide with the sawcut and that there are no metal obstacles beneath the cut. Always use both hands on the handles provided on the saw, so reducing the risk of the free hand making contact with the cutting edge of the blade. At the finish of the cut, keep the saw suspended away from the body until the blade stops revolving.

Additional safety factors include: keeping the power cable clear of the cutting action; not overloading the saw by forcing into the material; drawing the saw back if the saw-cut wanders from the line and carefully advancing to regain the line; wearing safety glasses or protective goggles; disconnecting the machine from the supply whilst making adjustments, or when not in use; keeping saw blades sharp and machines checked on a regular basis by a qualified electrical engineer; checking voltage and visual condition of saw, power cable and plug before use; working in safe, dry conditions.

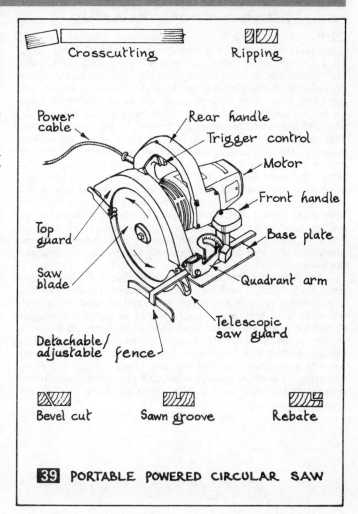

39 PORTABLE POWERED CIRCULAR SAW

PORTABLE ELECTRIC DRILLS AND PERCUSSION DRILLS

40 Providing there is a supply of electricity available on site, these tools have distinct advantages over manual hand drills. They are obviously faster and more efficient; they hold larger drills (according to their chuck size); they have no hand-turning operation that might restrict working in awkward corners; they can have, apart from a single speed, a two- or four-speed drive for drilling different materials; and last but not least, some of the two- and four-speed machines can be used for percussion drilling. This means that as well as having the lower speed for drilling masonry, the tool also has an integral mechanism for creating and delivering hammer blows to the material being drilled. Hence the name *hammer drill*, as they are often called in preference to *percussion drill*. The hammering action at about 500 blows per second, is hardly noticeable to the user, seeming to be little more than a dull vibration, but combined with the rotary drilling operation, the result is very impressive; clean-bored holes – controlled by a depth-gauge attachment on some machines – are speedily and effortlessly achieved in concrete and brickwork, etc.

The following safety factors should be observed: loose timber being drilled should be firmly held or clamped; reliable step ladders, trestles or orthodox platforms should be used when drilling walls at a high level; safety glasses or protective goggles should be worn; the machine should be disconnected from the supply whilst making adjustments, or when not in use; bits should be kept sharp; machines should be checked on a regular basis by a qualified electrical engineer; check voltage and visual condition of machine, power cable and plug before use; retain proper hold of drill until it stops revolving; work in safe, dry conditions.

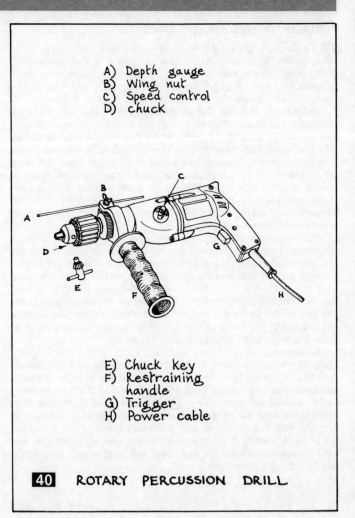

A) Depth gauge
B) Wing nut
C) Speed control
D) Chuck

E) Chuck key
F) Restraining handle
G) Trigger
H) Power cable

40   ROTARY PERCUSSION DRILL

CARTRIDGE TOOLS

41 These tools are of great value on certain first-fixing operations when fixing timber, steel sections and other materials to, mainly, structures of steel, concrete and brickwork. Originally, all fixings from these tools were fired by the high-velocity principle, whereby the nail travelled along the barrel at a velocity of about 500 metres per second. The nail, travelling at such a speed, was potentially lethal; hazards such as *through-penetration*, *free flighting* and *ricochets* via deflection, could occur through fixing into thin or weak materials, or striking hard aggregates or reinforcing rods.

To overcome these dangers, manufacturers have developed and use the low-velocity principle in their tools. This reduces the muzzle velocity from 500 m to between about 60 and 90 metres per second without any loss of power. This has been achieved by introducing a piston in the barrel between the cartridge at the rear and the nail in front. The nail, supported and guided by the cartridge-actuated piston, safely ceases its journey forward at the same time that the captive piston comes to rest.

The more sophisticated tools using this principle incorporate many new features including
(a) The facility to adjust the level of power without changing cartridges.
(b) An integrated silencer – which also improves balance and handling.
(c) Semi-automatic operation by means of magazined cartridges and integral loading lever, allowing repetitive fixings.
(d) Improved fixing quality.
(e) Low recoil due to the co-acting piston principle.
(f) The ability to accommodate a large range of fixings, including many different-sized nails and studs.

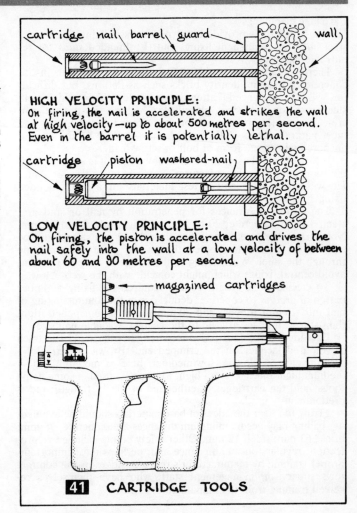

cartridge nail barrel guard wall

HIGH VELOCITY PRINCIPLE:
On firing, the nail is accelerated and strikes the wall at high velocity – up to about 500 metres per second. Even in the barrel it is potentially lethal.

cartridge piston washered-nail

LOW VELOCITY PRINCIPLE:
On firing, the piston is accelerated and drives the nail safely into the wall at a low velocity of between about 60 and 90 metres per second.

magazined cartridges

41 CARTRIDGE TOOLS

Cartridge tool fixings

42 Cartridge tools provide two types of basic fixing: (a) special steel *nails* for permanent fixings and (b) threaded *studs* for removable fixings.

There should be no problems if fixing into mild steel, in-situ concrete or medium-density bricks such as flettons, but difficulties will be experienced if attempts are made to fix into high yield steel, cast-iron, cast-steel, glazed tiles, high-density precast concrete, engineering bricks, soft bricks such as London Stocks and most natural stones – all of which may have to be drilled and anchored with some form of bolt or screw fixing.

If cartridge tool users are ever in any doubt, it is usually possible to arrange for a manufacturer's representative to visit a site. He will give advice and/or test materials for a recommended fixing system.

The correct allowances for penetration by nail or stud are: steel, 12 mm; concrete, 20 to 25 mm; brickwork, 25 to 37 mm. Note that if the steel is only 6 mm thick, 12 mm should still be allowed for penetration, even though the point will protrude through the steel. When fixing to the flange of a steel 'I' beam, avoid central fixings which might coincide with the web below.

To calculate the length of nail required for fixing a timber batten or *ground* to concrete, deduct 5 mm for countersinking of nail into 25 mm timber, add 20 mm for minimum penetration, then adjust, if necessary, up to the nearest available nail size.

Cartridges are colour-coded for strength, indicated by a touch of coloured lacquer on the crimped end. Brown = extra low, green = low, yellow = low/medium, blue = medium, red = medium/high, black = extra high. Magazines, used in some fixing tools, hold ten cartridges of either red or black strength; red is predominantly used.

Fixing too near the edges of base materials should be avoided, or spalling may occur; minimum distances are: concrete, 75 mm; brick, 63 mm; steel, 12 mm. Other safety points include eye protection, regular tool maintenance and, perhaps most important, proper training by manufacturer's representatives or the contractor's supervisory/management staff, who have themselves received training from the manufacturers.

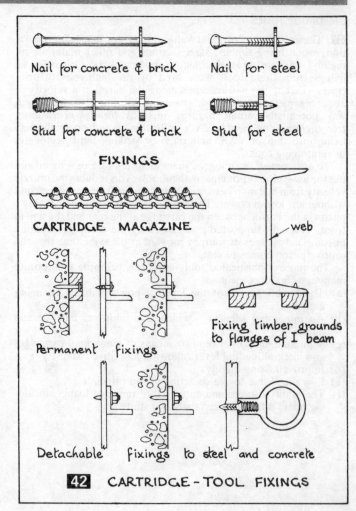

Nail for concrete & brick

Nail for steel

Stud for concrete & brick

Stud for steel

FIXINGS

CARTRIDGE MAGAZINE

web

Permanent fixings

Fixing timber grounds to flanges of I beam

Detachable   fixings   to steel and concrete

42 CARTRIDGE-TOOL FIXINGS

3 MAKING A CARPENTER'S TOOL BOX

The large amount of tools that carpenters need to perform their trade, demands some kind of box or bag in which to store them at the end of an operation, or in which to transport them when moving around. Whether it is one or the other is a matter of choice. Also, boxes of all shapes and sizes and a variety of bags (basses) and holdalls can be seen. Traditionally, the design and construction of the carpenter's tool box – still widely used in the original form – was made up as follows.

Carcase
1 This comprises the top, bottom and side material, which should be of selected softwood, straight-grained and free from large knots and other defects. To keep the weight of the box to a minimum, the finished thickness should be 13 mm, the width – ex. 175 mm – finished to 170 mm. The corners of the carcase should be formed with through-dovetail joints, glued together.

Cladding
The front and back of the box has 4 mm thick plywood glued and pinned to its edges.

Tray
A shallow tray or drawer, for holding small tools – especially edge-tools such as chisels – is made to fit the inside top of the box. This is supported by 21 × 9 mm finished hardwood side runners, glued and pinned or screwed to the sides of the box. The tray, with dovetailed corners and 6 mm thick cross-divisions, is made up from 70 × 9 mm finished material and 4 mm ply base.

Hinge fillets
These are glued and pinned to the inside faces of the lid and box to complete the structure and accommodate the hinges – and should be made from at least 28 × 16 mm softwood planed all round (p.a.r.).

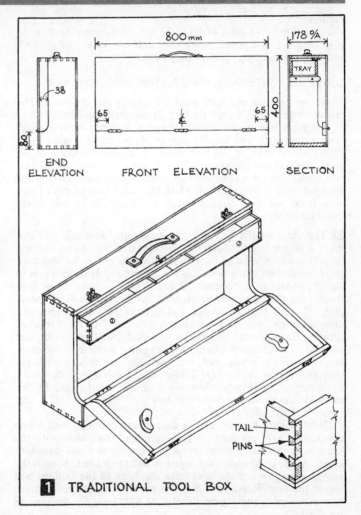

1 TRADITIONAL TOOL BOX

Fittings

These comprise 1½ pairs of 50 or 63 mm butt hinges or a piano strip hinge, a case handle, case clips and box lock – or padlock and hasp and staple, 75 mm safety pattern type.

CONSTRUCTION DETAILS: FORMING THROUGH-DOVETAILS

There are various methods used for setting out dovetails. The one described here is preferred for its simplicity and speed.

After cutting up the carcase material squarely with a panel saw to the length and height, with an allowance of 2 mm (1 mm each end) on each of the four pieces, mark the thickness of the material, plus the allowance – 13 + 1 mm – in from each end on two pieces only, one long and one short. Square these around the material with a sharp pencil. Mark the other two pieces of carcase from the two already marked. These marks are called shoulder lines.

2 The sides of the box are now ready for dovetailing. First, mark a centre line between the shoulder and the end of the timber. This line is used to contain the dividing points for the tails. Now decide how many dovetails are required and obtain a pair of sharp dividers or a compass. If you decide to have 5, as illustrated, the dividers must be stepped out by trial-and-error stepping, 5½ steps from one edge and 5½ from the other. Then the dovetail angle, set on a bevel to a ratio of 1 in 6, is marked through these points. The easiest way to think of this setting-out method, is to remember that ½ a divider step more than the number of dovetails is required, i.e. 1 dovetail, 1½ divider steps (or spacings) across the timber; 2 dovetails, 2½ spacings; 3 dovetails, 3½ spacings, etc. If larger dovetails than pins are required by this method, simply step out the dividers until less than half a step remains at the edge.

Next, square the tails across the top, cut carefully with a fine saw (tenon saw will suffice), remove outside shoulders with the same saw, the inside shoulders with a coping saw and bevelled-edge chisels. Hold each joint together and mark the tails onto the end-grain. Square these lines onto the faces of the bottom and top of the box. Remember that it is the dovetail shapes that are now removed – and repeat the cutting operation for the pins as for the tails.

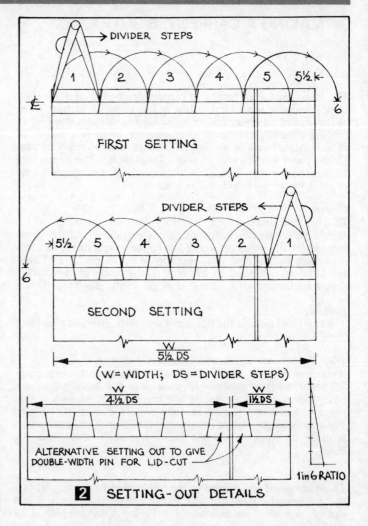

DIVIDER STEPS

1   2   3   4   5   5½   6

FIRST SETTING

DIVIDER STEPS

5½   5   4   3   2   1   6

SECOND SETTING

$\dfrac{W}{5½\ DS}$

(W = WIDTH; DS = DIVIDER STEPS)

$\dfrac{W}{4½\ DS}$ $\dfrac{W}{1½\ DS}$

ALTERNATIVE SETTING OUT TO GIVE DOUBLE-WIDTH PIN FOR LID-CUT

1 in 6 RATIO

2 SETTING-OUT DETAILS

METHOD OF CONSTRUCTION

3 The thin carcase material is very prone to distortion across its width, known as cupping – especially if the growth rings are tangential to the face.

4 For this reason, the joints should be formed as quickly as possible and the carcase glued together and checked diagonally for squareness.

5 A gauge line representing the eventual edge of the lid, can now be marked – or may have been marked earlier to assist in setting out the dovetails – and should terminate as a quadrant shape 80 mm up from the base. This quadrant shape *only*, should be cut on each side with a coping saw before cladding.

The plywood for the front and back, having been cut slightly oversize by a few millimetres, is then glued and pinned (18 mm panel pins at approximately 75 mm centres (c/c)) into position, transforming the assembly into an inaccessible box. The box is then 'cleaned up' with a smoothing plane to a flat finish on the base, sides and top.

By careful use of a tenon saw – or fine panel saw – working from each top corner, across the top and down the sides to meet the cut quadrants, then across the ply front, the lid is cut and released. The hinge fillets – including the end abutments – are then glued into position and pinned through the face of the ply. When set, the lid can be hinged and the box – including the sawn edges of the lid – 'cleaned up' with glass paper.

The handle, case clips and hasp and staple can now be fitted, prior to fixing a 30 × 6 mm p.a.r. hardwood fillet to the inside lock-edge of the box. This must project about 6 to 9 mm to help transfer the weight of the box – when lifted – to the lid.

Finally, again using through-dovetails, or simple cross-rebates, the tray is made with one or two cross-divisions, to the inside length, minus 2 mm for tolerance. Turn-buttons for saw handles can be made and glued to the lid to hold the crosscut and panel saws.

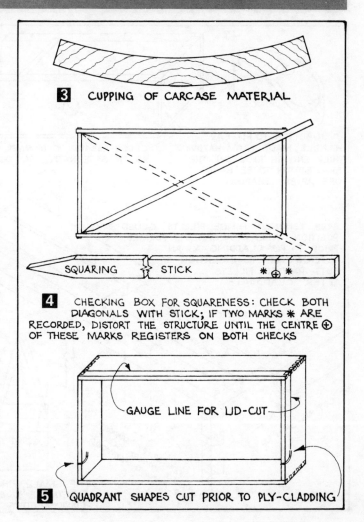

3 CUPPING OF CARCASE MATERIAL

SQUARING STICK

4 CHECKING BOX FOR SQUARENESS: CHECK BOTH DIAGONALS WITH STICK; IF TWO MARKS ✳ ARE RECORDED, DISTORT THE STRUCTURE UNTIL THE CENTRE ⊕ OF THESE MARKS REGISTERS ON BOTH CHECKS

GAUGE LINE FOR LID-CUT

5 QUADRANT SHAPES CUT PRIOR TO PLY-CLADDING

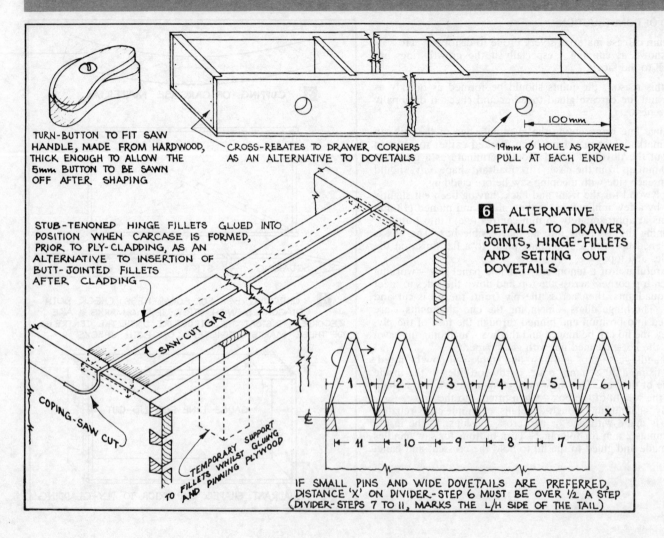

TURN-BUTTON TO FIT SAW HANDLE, MADE FROM HARDWOOD, THICK ENOUGH TO ALLOW THE 5mm BUTTON TO BE SAWN OFF AFTER SHAPING

CROSS-REBATES TO DRAWER CORNERS AS AN ALTERNATIVE TO DOVETAILS

19mm Ø HOLE AS DRAWER-PULL AT EACH END

100mm

STUB-TENONED HINGE FILLETS GLUED INTO POSITION WHEN CARCASE IS FORMED, PRIOR TO PLY-CLADDING, AS AN ALTERNATIVE TO INSERTION OF BUTT-JOINTED FILLETS AFTER CLADDING

SAW-CUT GAP

COPING-SAW CUT

TEMPORARY SUPPORT TO FILLETS WHILST GLUING AND PINNING PLYWOOD

6 ALTERNATIVE DETAILS TO DRAWER JOINTS, HINGE-FILLETS AND SETTING OUT DOVETAILS

1   2   3   4   5   6

X

11   10   9   8   7

IF SMALL PINS AND WIDE DOVETAILS ARE PREFERRED, DISTANCE 'X' ON DIVIDER-STEP 6 MUST BE OVER ½ A STEP (DIVIDER-STEPS 7 TO 11, MARKS THE L/H SIDE OF THE TAIL)

4 MAKING SMALL PLANT ON SITE

SAW STOOL

1 A carpenter's saw stool, sometimes called a horse or a trestle, has a few variations in design, but the one shown at **1** is most commonly used. The length and height can also vary, although the height should not be less than that shown, otherwise on hand rip-sawing operations – when the saw should be at a steep angle of about 60° to 70° – the end of the saw may hit the floor.

The material used is usually softwood and can be a sawn finish or p.a.r. The latter reduces the risk of picking up splinters when handling the stool. Material sizes also vary, often according to what may or may not be available on site, or again for design reasons and consideration of the weight factor of the stool.

Typical sizes for a sturdy stool are given in the illustrations, showing the top as ex. 100 × 50 mm, legs ex. 75 × 50 mm, end cleats 6, 9, or 12 mm plywood.

Angles of legs are not critical to a degree and are usually based on the safe angle-of-lean used on ladders, which is to a ratio of 4 in 1 (4 : 1). This refers to a slope or gradient measured by a vertical rise of four units over a horizontal distance of one unit. This ratio works out to be approximately 76 degrees.

Some tradespeople choose to incorporate a tray within the leg structure, to act as a nail box. The tray, which is sub-divided to contain a variety of nails, screws, etc. has shallow sides of about 50 to 75 mm depth, plywood base, and is usually fixed halfway up the legs on cross- or longitudinal bearers. The advantages of this combination stool/nail box are outweighed by the increased weight factor, restricted access to nails, trapping of sawdust and cleaning-out difficulties.

By following very basic criteria and guesswork, saw stools are often roughly made without any regard for the geometry involved. This is partly to save time, but also reflects an ignorance of the subject. Making a saw stool is a quick and simple operation, joinery and geometry-wise, although any given method might seem more difficult in explanation than it actually is in practice.

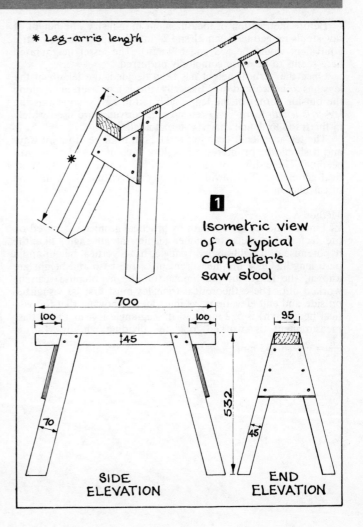

* Leg-arris length

1

Isometric view of a typical carpenter's saw stool

700
100   100
45

SIDE ELEVATION

95
532
70
45

END ELEVATION

Before metrication of measurement in industry, the height of saw stools ranged between 21 and 24 in. (the approximate metric equivalent would be 532 and 610 mm). The lesser height used here seems to be more commonly preferred.

Once the vertical height has been decided, the length of the legs has to be worked out. Basically, this is a measurement along the outside corner of the leg – indicated in **1** * – known as the *leg-arris length* (*arris* is a French/Latin-derived word used widely in the trade to define sharp, external angles).

The leg-arris length can be worked out in three different ways and it should be of interest to explore each of these before proceeding. These different methods can be identified as: (A) practical geometry; (B) drawing-board geometry; and (C) a method of calculation.

Method A

2 Finding the leg-arris length by **practical geometry** is based on the fact that a piece of timber leaning at an angle, like the hypotenuse of a right-angled triangle, has a vertical height and a base length. Once the measurement of the base and height are known, the length of the timber (on the hypotenuse) can be worked out. These theoretical triangles must first be visualized on side and end elevations, as illustrated. Knowing that the vertical height (vh) is 532 mm and the leg-angle is 4 in 1, the base measurement is worked out by dividing vh by 4, i.e. $\frac{vh}{4} = \frac{532}{4} = 133$ mm.

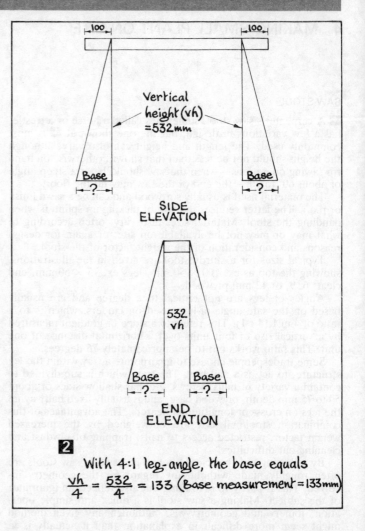

SIDE ELEVATION

END ELEVATION

2 With 4:1 leg-angle, the base equals $\frac{vh}{4} = \frac{532}{4} = 133$ (Base measurement = 133mm)

3 Now that the base measurement of the side and end elevation triangles is known to be 133 mm, this information can be used to find the obscure base measurement of the leg-arris triangle. Because the leg is leaning at the same angle in both elevations, the leg-arris base must be a 45° diagonal within a square of 133 × 133 mm.

All that needs to be done, therefore, is to form a true square with these measurements, draw a diagonal line from corner to corner and measure its length. The product is the base measurement of the leg-arris triangle. This measurement is then applied to the base of another right-angled setting out, the stool's vertical height added and the resultant diagonal on the hypotenuse measured to produce the true leg-arris length.

4 Two practical ways of doing this, are to use a steel roofing square (now called a metric rafter square by the makers), or to use the right-angled corner of a piece of hardboard or plywood.

As illustrated, the base measurement (b) of 133 mm is set on each side of the angle to enable the diagonal (c), the base of the leg-arris triangle, to be measured. This measurement, 188 mm, forms the base of another setting out on the square or hardboard, in relation to the vertical height of the stool (a), 532 mm, being placed on the opposite side of the angle. The diagonal (d) is then measured to produce the true leg-arris length at 564 mm to the nearest millimetre.

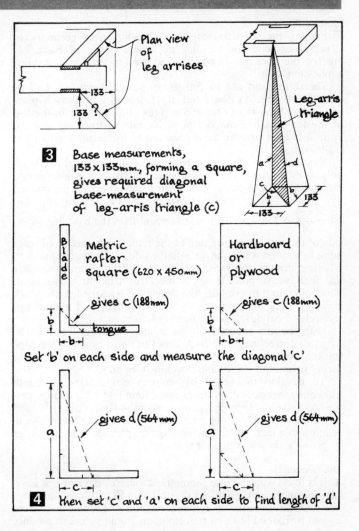

Plan view of leg arrises

Leg-arris triangle

3 Base measurements, 133 × 133 mm., forming a square, gives required diagonal base-measurement of leg-arris triangle (c)

Blade

Metric rafter square (620 × 450 mm)

gives c (188 mm)

tongue

Hardboard or plywood

gives c (188 mm)

Set 'b' on each side and measure the diagonal 'c'

gives d (564 mm)

gives d (564 mm)

4 then set 'c' and 'a' on each side to find length of 'd'

Method B

5 Finding the leg-arris length by **drawing-board geometry** is a useful exercise for building up a knowledge of basic geometry, but does not, of course, lend itself to site (or workshop) application.

The setting out can be full size or scaled down to a half or quarter full size. As illustrated, the first step is to draw a part-plan view of the stool's top, 95 mm (ex. 100) wide, with the top of the leg-arris line marked at a, 100 mm in from the end, b. Point a is then squared across the top to locate the start of the leg-housings.

Next, the legs' theoretical base line, shown here on two sides only, is established. This is determined by the legs leaning in two directions at an angle of 4 in 1, so that vertical height divided by four, equals base measurement of leg-spread, i.e. $\frac{vh}{4} = \frac{532}{4} = 133$ mm. This measurement fixes the base line to the side of the stool as shown and at the return end, measured from point a, to form a right angle with the side. The leg-arris line a to c is then drawn; and at 90° to this, rising from point a, another line is drawn to point d, set at the vertical height of the stool. Now join c to d to establish the developed leg-arris length. Mark point e, equal to stool-top thickness from d, and extend out squarely to cut developed leg-arris at e′.

Using point c as centre for the compass, transfer d to f and e′ to g to intersect with line b–f. Join f to c and establish leg-edge thickness parallel to f–c. Extend horizontal lines from f and g to form birdsmouth angles and developed leg edge.

To develop the shape of the end cleat, mark its depth (200 mm) vertically down from g and form line k through n, parallel to line c–o. Establish point 1, equal to the plotting of f, and strike a line from l, in line with o at base of legs, to form m–n in relation to a final line from g through m, parallel to k–n. Angles g–m–n–k show the true cleat shape.

Dihedral angle

This is to do with the true geometrical shape of the legs and is explained on the next page. As illustrated in **5** with a as centre for the compass, describe an arc tangential (at 90°) to line c–d to cut c–a at h. Extend line i–a to form point j. Join j–h–i to produce a dihedral angle of 94°.

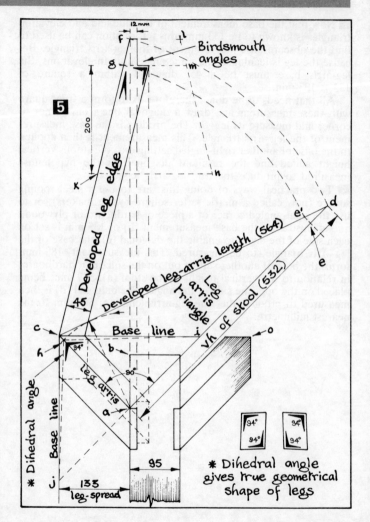

6 As indicated in the setting out covered in **5**, the true geometrical, sectional shape of the legs is rhomboidal (rectangular, with opposite sides equal in length and parallel to each other, but with all angles out of true). This shape is to meet the dihedral angle created by the legs' angles-of-lean. Perhaps an appreciation of the dihedral angle can best be understood by holding a try-square (preferably a steel roofing-square) in a truly horizontal position, against a square section of timber positioned to lean at angles similar to the saw-stool leg. As illustrated at **6**, tapered gaps showing on the face side and edge of the leg will prove that the dihedral angle has changed from 90° for a leg in the upright position, to 94° for a leg leaning at angles of 76° (4 in 1) on two elevations.

In practice, to simplify the work, the legs are left in a true rectangular shape – but it must be realized that this causes a slight misfit of the birdsmouthed legs into the housings and an unequal seating of the end cleats onto the leg edges. The latter is the most noticeable, if viewed from the underside.

These slight irregularities are not enough in themselves to warrant the extra time and effort in making the legs to a rhomboidal shape. The strength of the stool is not impaired to any appreciable degree, nor the visual standard of finish.

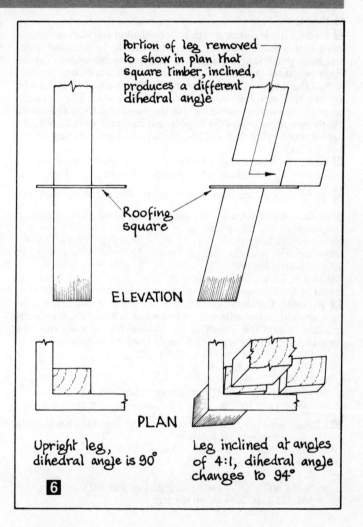

Portion of leg removed to show in plan that square timber, inclined, produces a different dihedral angle

Roofing square

ELEVATION

Upright leg, dihedral angle is 90°

PLAN

Leg inclined at angles of 4:1, dihedral angle changes to 94°

6

Method C

7 Finding the leg-arris length by **a method of calculation**, entails using Pythagoras's theorem, the square on the hypotenuse (c) of a right-angled triangle is equal to the sum of the squares on the other two sides (a and b); i.e. $a^2 + b^2 = c^2$. Thereby it is possible to find the length of the hypotenuse if the length of sides a and b are known. Once the sum of the *square* (represented by '2' raised up after the number, meaning that the number is to be multiplied by it's own number) on the hypotenuse has been worked out, the square root of that sum will give the length of the hypotenuse (c); i.e. $\sqrt{c^2} = c$.

8 First, the base measurement of the leg spread must be determined by dividing the vertical height by four, i.e. $\dfrac{vh}{4} = \dfrac{532}{4} = 133$ mm base measurement. The following abbreviations have been used in the illustration showing the triangular formation of the leg spread:

vh = vertical height
lat = leg-arris triangle
lal = leg-arris length
bm = 4 in 1 base measurement
bmlat = base measurement of leg-arris triangle

9 By using Pythagoras's theorem, the base measurements are now applied to the adjacent and opposite sides of the leg-spread triangle to find the length of the hypotenuse, namely the base measurement of the leg-arris triangle (bmlat), as follows:
$c^2 = 133^2 + 133^2$ $(c^2 = 133 \times 133 + 133 \times 133)$
$c^2 = 17\ 689 + 17\ 689$
$c^2 = 35\ 378$
$c = \sqrt{35\ 378}$ (c = the square root of 35 378)
$c = 188.09$ (say 188) bmlat = 188 mm

10 Finally, the leg-arris length is found by applying vh and bmlat to the same formula, as follows:
$c^2 = 532^2 + 188^2$ $(c^2 = 532 \times 532 + 188 \times 188)$
$c^2 = 283\ 024 + 35\ 378$
$c^2 = 318\ 402$
$c = \sqrt{318\ 402}$ (c = the square root of 318 402)
$c = 564.271$ (say 564) lal = 564 mm

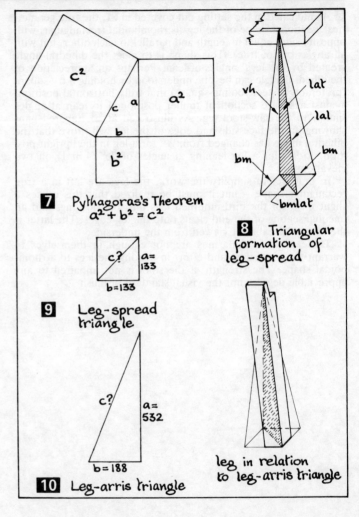

7 Pythagoras's Theorem
$a^2 + b^2 = c^2$

8 Triangular formation of leg-spread

9 Leg-spread triangle

10 Leg-arris triangle

leg in relation to leg-arris triangle

Now that the true leg-arris length has been determined by one of the foregoing methods, at least another 35 mm plus 11 mm cutting tolerance has to be added to the leg as an allowance for the angled setting out involved. Length of legs, therefore, equals true leg-arris length, 564 mm, plus 46 mm tolerances, equals 610 mm.

11 Legs and stool top can now be cut to length, ready for marking out. The marking out can either be done with a carpenter's bevel (or bevels), or with a purpose-made template. As illustrated, the 4 in 1/1 in 4 angles are set out against the square corner of a piece of hardboard or plywood to a selected size. 300 mm and 75 mm are advisable as a minimum ratio if the setting out is to be cut off and used as a template in itself. If carpenters' bevels are to be used, set up one at 4 in 1 and the other at 1 in 4, as illustrated. If only one bevel is available, set and use at the 4 in 1 (76°) angle before resetting for use at the 1 in 4 (14°) angle.

12 An alternative way of setting out the two required angles, to enable a carpenter's bevel to be set up, is shown at **12**. First, mark a square line from point a on the face of a straightedge or on the face of the stool-top material. Then, from point a, mark point b at 4 cm (40 mm) and point c at 1 cm (10 mm). Draw line c through b to establish the first required angle of 4 in 1 (76°). From point a, mark point d at 1 cm and point e from either side of a at 4 cm. Draw line e through d to establish the second angle of 1 in 4 (14°).

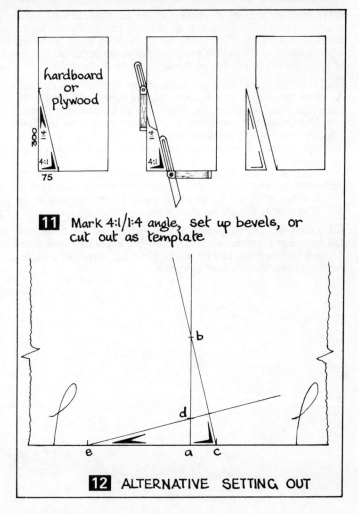

11 Mark 4:1/1:4 angle, set up bevels, or cut out as template

12 ALTERNATIVE SETTING OUT

13a Before attempting to mark out the birdsmouth cuts, it is essential to identify and mark the starting point on each leg to avoid confusion. As illustrated, this point is on each inside-leg edge, about 5 or 6 mm down, and relates to the uppermost point of the splay cut in relation to the top surface of the stool.

13b From this point, the 4 in 1 angle always slopes down on edge A, turns the corner and, likewise, slopes down on face-side B, turns again and this time slopes up on edge C, and up on back-face D to meet the first point on face-edge A. So, on the four sides of each leg, the marking sequence leading from one line to the other, is two slopes down, two slopes up, back to zero point on leg-edge A.

Note that in the illustration, the shaded areas represent the timber on the waste side of the cut. Graphic demarcation such as this is often practised by carpenters and joiners to reduce the risk of removing the wrong area of material.

14 Zero point can be quickly determined on each leg by placing the four legs together, with the inside-leg edges and back-faces (A and D) touching, and by marking the top corner of each leg on the middle intersection, as shown.

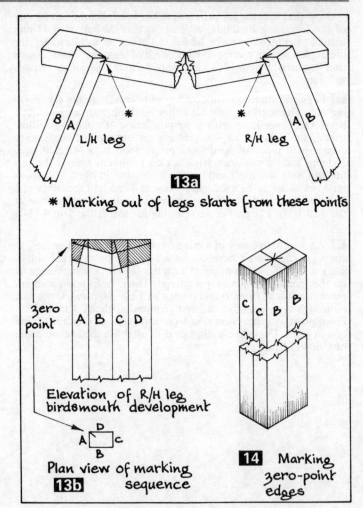

13a

* Marking out of legs starts from these points

Elevation of R/H leg birdsmouth development

Plan view of marking sequence
13b

14 Marking zero-point edges

15 By using a template positioned on its 4 in 1 (76°) angle, surfaces A, B, C and D of the leg are first marked as illustrated here and as described in **13b** .

16 Then, back to surface A, the template is again positioned and marked on the 4 in 1 angle, set at 48 mm down, measured at right angles to the first line. This represents the stool-top thickness, 45 mm, plus 3 mm to offset the fact that the stool-top thickness registers geometrically at a greater depth on the 4 in 1 angled legs. Next, measure 12 mm in on the top line to represent the beak of the birdsmouth cut and use the 1 in 4 (14°) angle of the template to mark the line as shown.

17 To complete the marking out of the first leg, the lower line on surface A, representing the stool-top thickness, is picked up on surface B by the template and marked parallel to the line above; picked up on surface C and again marked parallel to the line above, then the 1 in 4 (14°) angle is marked in at 12 mm to complete the beak of the birdsmouth (this birdsmouth marking is on the opposite side of the one marked on surface A). Finally, the lip of the birdsmouth is picked up from C and marked on surface D, yet again parallel to the line above.

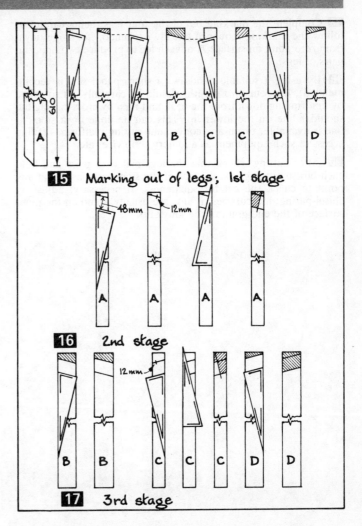

15 Marking out of legs; 1st stage

16 2nd stage

17 3rd stage

18 Complete the marking out of the four legs, being careful to follow the marking sequence already explained, i.e. slope down from zero point on surface A of each leg to produce two opposite pairs of legs.

19 By using a suitable handsaw (a sharp panel saw is recommended), the four birdsmouths should be carefully cut to shape by first ripping down from the beak and then by cross-cutting the shoulder line on the lower lip. This can be done on a stool, if one is available, or on any convenient cutting platform – failing access to such equipment as a joinery-shop vice, etc.

20 After cutting, check that the legs match in pairs and hold each birdsmouth against the side of the stool-top material at any point to check the cut for squareness. If necessary, adjust by chisel-paring; inaccuracies, if any, are usually found on the inner surface of the end grain of the lower lip.

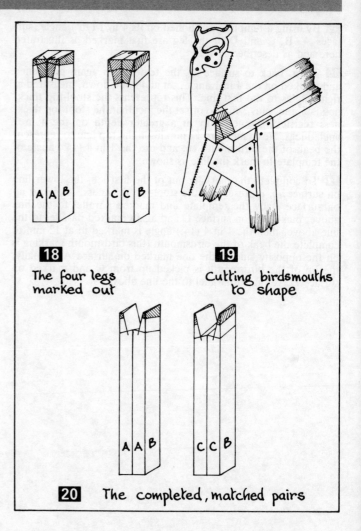

18 The four legs marked out

19 Cutting birdsmouths to shape

20 The completed, matched pairs

21 Next, as illustrated, the birdsmouthed legs are held in position on the side of the stool top, 100 mm in from the ends, and the sides marked to indicate the housings.

22 When marked and squared onto the faceside and underside, the housings are gauged to 12 mm depth on both sides of the stool top, ready for housing. The angled sides of the housings are then cut with a tenon saw or a panel saw and pared out with a wide bevel-edged chisel. The recommended chiselling technique, for safety and efficiency, is to pare down – either by hand pressure or with the aid of a mallet – onto a solid bench or boarded surface from alternate faces of the stool top.

23 The stool top can now be set aside and the legs prepared for fixings, if screws are to be used. As indicated, two or three fixings may be used and are judged rather than marked for position. However, for strength, the fixings should neither be too near the edges nor too close together. Shank holes should be drilled and countersunk for, say, 50 mm × 10 gauge screws. If nails are used instead of screws, 63 to 75 mm round-head wire (r.h.w.) nails are preferred.

Take care when screwing or driving-in fixings, to ensure that they are parallel to the stool-top's surface, i.e. at a 4 in 1 angle to the surface of the legs.

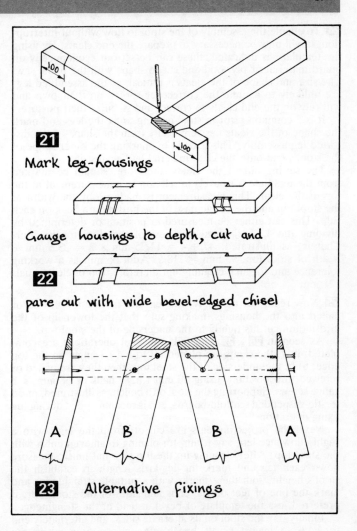

21 Mark leg-housings

Gauge housings to depth, cut and

22 pare out with wide bevel-edged chisel

23 Alternative fixings

24 To enable the assembly of the stool to flow without interruption, it will now be necessary to prepare the end cleats. By using the template as indicated, these can be set out economically on board material or plywood and cut to shape with the panel saw. The size and shape of the cleats is critical, as the assembled legs are unlikely to assume the correct leg-spread on their own and will rely on the end cleats to correct and stabilize their posture.

It is a common error in stool-making to fix the legs and mark the shape of the cleats unscientifically from the shape of the distorted leg assembly. This is done by marking the outer shape of the stool's end onto the cleat material laid against it.

The setting out of the cleats, therefore, should be marked from the template (or bevel) in relation to a measurement at the top of the cleat. This measurement is made up by the width of the stool top and the visible base of the birdsmouth beak on each side. This can either be measured in position or determined by dividing the 4 : 1 diagonal thickness of the stool top by four. That is, as illustrated, $47 \div 4 = 11.75$ mm $\times 2 = 23.5$ mm $+$ width of stool top, 95 mm $= 118.5$. Add 2.5 mm as a working tolerance and for final cleaning up, therefore, top of cleat equals 121 mm.

25 Now ready for assembly, the legs are fitted and screwed or nailed into the housings, making sure that the lower lip of the birdsmouth cut fits tightly to the underside of the stool top.

As seen in **26** , **27** and **28** , the final operations are completed; first, the cleats are planed off to a 4 : 1 angle on the top edge, to fit the underside of the stool top, then they are nailed or screwed into position, using 50 mm r.h.w. nails or 38 mm × 8 gauge screws. Supporting the stool on a bench, as illustrated, or on trestle-suspended scaffold-boards, etc. is recommended during the fixing operation.

Next, the projecting ears are cut off from the legs, with a slight allowance left, say 1 mm, for planing to an even finish with the stool top. After cleaning-up the top to a flat finish, measure down each leg and mark the leg-arris length to establish the stool's height. Join these marks with a suitable straightedge and mark the line of feet on the ends and sides of the stool – or, if preferred, use the template or bevel instead of the straightedge.

Finally, lay the stool on its alternate sides, and alternately end for end, up against a wall, bench, etc. and carefully cut off the waste from the legs with a panel saw. Clean off sides of cleats, etc. to finish.

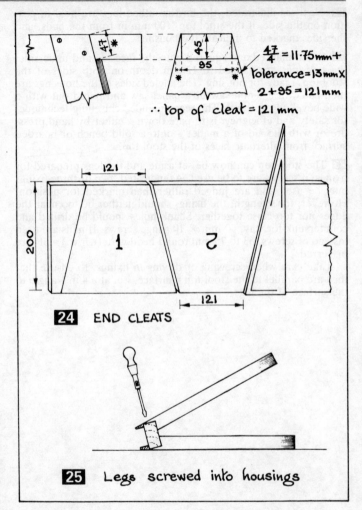

$$\frac{47}{4} = 11.75\text{mm} +$$
$$\text{tolerance} = 13\text{mm} \times$$
$$2 + 95 = 121\text{mm}$$
$$\therefore \text{top of cleat} = 121\text{ mm}$$

24 END CLEATS

25 Legs screwed into housings

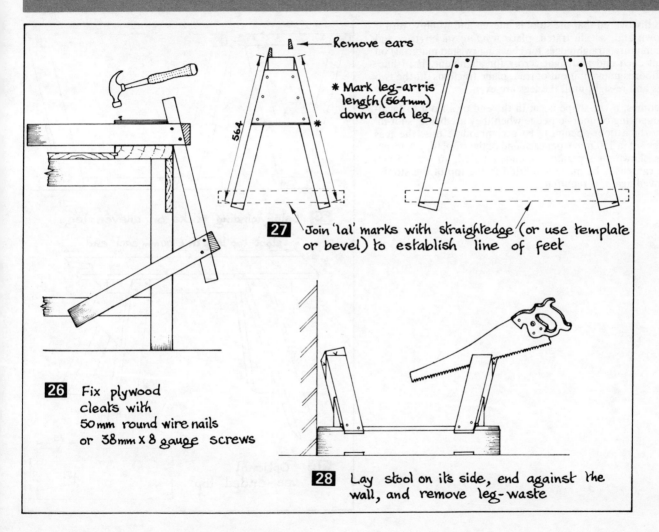

← Remove ears

* Mark leg-arris
length (564mm)
down each leg

564

27 Join 'lal' marks with straightedge (or use template or bevel) to establish line of feet

26 Fix plywood cleats with 50mm round wire nails or 38mm × 8 gauge screws

28 Lay stool on its side, end against the wall, and remove leg-waste

29 If it is discovered that the stool is uneven and wobbly, turn it upside down and, as illustrated, place *winding sticks* (true and parallel miniature straightedges for checking twisted material) on the feet at each end and sight across for alignment. If in line, then the floor is uneven; if out of true, plane fractions off the two 'high' legs and re-sight until the legs are even.

30 Sometimes, a vee-shape is cut in the end of a stool to facilitate the steadying of doors-on-edge when they are being 'shot-in' (planed to fit a door-opening). To accommodate this, the legs ought to be set in 150 mm from each end of the stool top. Alternatively, as shown, a separate vee-ended board, of ex. 25 mm material, can easily be made and fitted to the top of the stool – and removed again, if required.

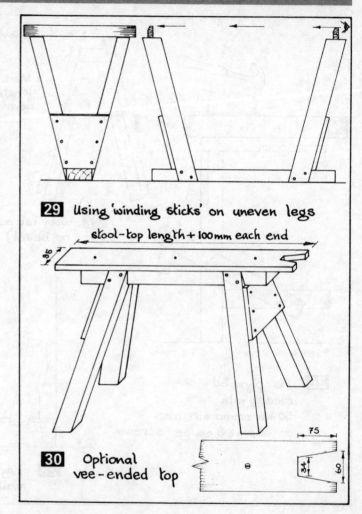

29 Using 'winding sticks' on uneven legs

stool-top length + 100mm each end

96

30 Optional vee-ended top

75

3

6

SAW HORSE

31 Special vices can be used for saw sharpening, but more commonly – especially on site – wooden frames known as *saw horses* or *saw stocks* are used. The material is usually softwood and can be of a sawn finish or p.a.r. The wooden jaws, made from ex. 75 × 25 mm material, which hold the saw in the frame are known as *saw chops*. The frame is made up of two ex. 75 × 50 mm (or 100 × 50 mm) stiles or legs, ex. 75 × 25 mm cross-rails on each side, acting as foot and knee rails, optional top rails above the knee rails and an optional diagonal brace.

The diagonal brace is usually seen on site-made horses, to strengthen the simple construction of the surface-nailed rails. On shop-made horses, the rails are usually housed and screwed into the stiles and so there is no need for a brace. Also, on shop-made horses, the saw chops are often made of hardwood and a coach bolt is inserted through the edge of each stile, near the top, to offset the tendency of splitting the legs when the saw chops are driven in to the vee-cuts to hold the saw.

The first step in making a saw horse is to prepare the stiles. Because it is important that a person takes up the correct posture at the horse, the height is critical and ideally should be varied to suit the individual. The total height of 1.050 m given here would be suitable for a tall person of about 1.830 m (6 ft). The vee-cut to receive the saw chops should be marked out in relation to the vee-shaped housings to be cut in the chops themselves. The vee-shape should promote a slow wedge action, as opposed to a less acute angle that would not take such a good grip on wedge shapes driven in to it. At the base of the vee-cuts, a saw cut is made to the depths shown, to house the upturned blade of the saws being sharpened – and one stile (on the side chosen to take the heel of the saws) must have a further slot of about 12 mm width to accommodate back-saws such as tenon saws.

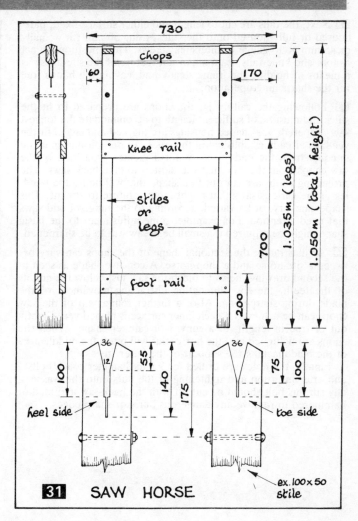

31 SAW HORSE

32 Next, the rails are cut to length and either surface-fixed, part-housed or fully-housed onto the stiles, using 50 mm r.h.w. nails or 45 mm × 10 gauge countersunk screws. Their position, to act as foot and knee rails, is an important feature of the site-horse as a means of holding the frame steady and leaving the hands free for the sharpening operation.

33 Following the rail-fixing, the chops are prepared to fit the stiles and must be of sufficient length to accommodate the longest saw. Tapered, vee-shaped housings are marked and cut to fit the vee-cuts already established in the stiles. These housings must be unequal from the ends to allow for a greater projection of the saw chops from the stile that was slotted to take back-saws. The projecting chops are cut out to a shape that will house the handles of the various saws that might require future treatment. This shape can vary, or be varied, according to the range of odd saws that need attention. For example, some adjustment to the basic shape might be required if a small bead saw was to be sharpened.

34 As illustrated, the sectional shape of the chops can vary between a site-horse and a shop-horse. A concave shape as seen in the second drawing, helps to pinch the saw just below the gullets of the teeth, thereby eliminating distracting movement of the blade during sharpening. Also, a further refinement of the saw chops can be achieved if each inner surface is planed very slightly out of true in length, to a convex or camber shape. When the chops are tightened into the horse, this will pinch the middle area of the blade lacking the support of the outer stiles.

Finally, the holes are drilled for 9 mm diameter coach bolts – and after insertion and tightening of the nuts onto the washers, any surplus bolt should be cut off with the hack-saw and filed or hammered to remove any dangerous burrs or sharp edges.

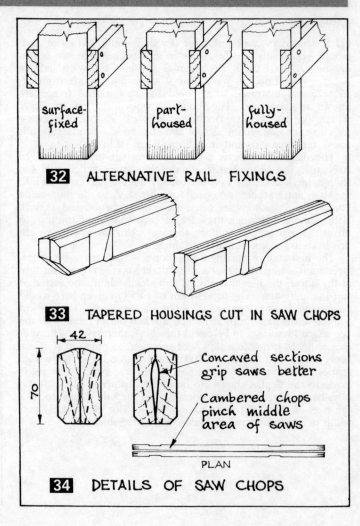

32 ALTERNATIVE RAIL FIXINGS

33 TAPERED HOUSINGS CUT IN SAW CHOPS

Concaved sections grip saws better

Cambered chops pinch middle area of saws

PLAN

34 DETAILS OF SAW CHOPS

NAIL BOXES

Nail boxes appear in all shapes and sizes and vary between very simple – and often very rough – constructions where all joints are butted and nailed, to more elaborate forms with dovetailed corners, housed cross-divisions and shaped handles.

The dovetailed type are not common in industry, but serve as a very useful jointing exercise for apprentices, trainees or students and can also provide a presentable nail box for one's own workshop. Apart from this, the simple, easier-constructed box serves its purpose well enough – whether in the workshop or out on site. This purpose is to provide a manageable means of transporting a sufficient supply of nails of different size and type from one work-location to another.

Generally speaking, on first-fixing operations, the compartments in the box can be fewer and therefore larger, to house such nail sizes as 75 and 100 mm r.h.w. nails, whereas, on second-fixing operations, more compartments are usually needed to house a greater variety of smaller nails such as 38 and 50 mm oval nails, etc.

Dovetailed nail box
35 The one shown is built up of 70 × 12 mm finish sides and ends, jointed together with through-dovetails on each corner. It has a 145 × 21 mm finish handle division housed into the ends to one-third the end thickness, and 6 mm plywood cross-divisions housed 4 mm into the sides and handle-division. The 130 × 32 mm slot for the handle is drilled out with a 32 mm diameter centre bit, chisel-pared and chamfered to a clean finish. The assembly is then glued together and checked for squareness before the 4 mm plywood base is glued and pinned into position.

Site nail box
36 As illustrated, this is built up of 10 to 12 mm plywood sides, ends and cross-divisions, with ex. 50 × 25 mm handle morticed into each end, and 4 or 6 mm plywood base. The assembly is nailed together unglued with 38 or 50 mm r.h.w. nails. The cross-halved plywood divider is dropped loosely into the box, without side-housings, and fixed through the sides and ends with oval or wire nails – and, finally, the handle is inserted and pinned or screwed through the top of each box-end.

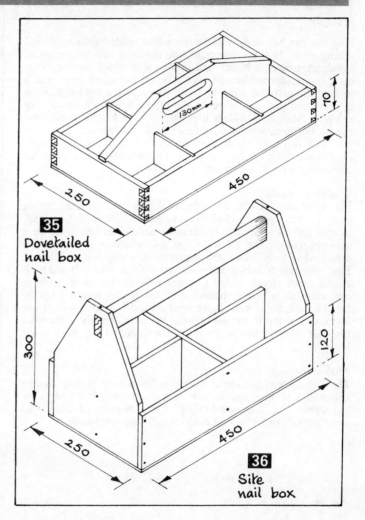

35 Dovetailed nail box

36 Site nail box

HOP-UPS

Hop-ups can be used by plasterers when rendering/floating and setting walls. In these situations, the plasterer uses a floating or skimming trowel, a handboard (hawk) with which to repeatedly carry the plaster to the wall, and a 'board and stand' from which to feed the material onto the hawk. Because the loaded hawk is in one hand and the trowel in the other, he cannot easily – or safely – climb step-ladders if plastering to a height beyond his reach. Furthermore, step-ladders inhibit the plastering action. So, there is a need for an easily-movable (repositioned by foot), easily-ascendable (stair-like rise), and non-restrictive piece of equipment such as a hop-up.

Traditional hop-up
37 As illustrated, this is simple in design and structure, being built up of square-edged or tongued-and-grooved boarding, cleated and clench-nailed (protruding nail-points bent over for a stronger fixing). The 100×25 mm sawn boarding shown here, is arranged to form a two-step hop-up with a step rise of 225 mm. First, two side-frames are constructed of vertical boards and horizontal cleats clench-nailed together with 56 mm r.h.w. nails or cut, clasp nails. These frames are then joined together by the tread boards being nailed into position and two cross-rails at low level, one at the front, the other at the back. Finally, a diagonal brace of 50×25 mm or 75×25 mm section is also fixed at the back.

Modern hop-up
38 The modern version of a hop-up shown here, is simplified by using 20 mm plywood as side frames, normal boarded steps, cross-rails and diagonal bracing. On a hop-up of this width (600 mm) 20 mm plywood could also be used as treads.

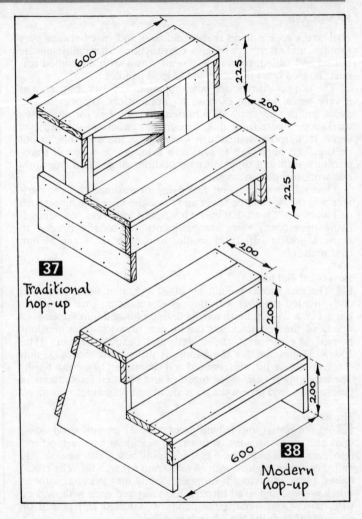

37 Traditional hop-up

38 Modern hop-up

BOARD AND STAND

A board and stand is also a piece of site equipment used by plasterers. It acts as a platform upon which the mixed plastering materials are deposited and are more easily trowel-fed onto the hawk placed under the board's edge. There are two types of stand, one being rigid in construction, the other, folding. Both have a similar, separate mortar board which lays in position on top without any attachment to the stand.

Rigid stand

39 The height of this can vary between 675 to 750 mm and the width and depth is usually about 600 × 600 mm. This allows the board to overhang the stand to facilitate the loading of the hawk. The material used can be p.a.r. or sawn softwood. First, 50 × 50 mm legs and 75 × 25 mm rails are cut to length to form two frames. On each frame, one rail is nailed to the top of the legs, the other is nailed about 100 mm clear of the bottom. Each frame is then braced diagonally with 50 × 25 mm or 75 × 25 mm bracing material and the two frames joined with the remaining cross-rails at top and bottom. Finally, the two remaining braces are fixed. 50 to 63 mm r.h.w. nails are used throughout.

This type of stand is quite common on plastering contracts where an extensive amount of traditional wet plastering techniques are being used, but on other smaller jobs, the folding stand and board illustrated on the next page are sometimes more convenient.

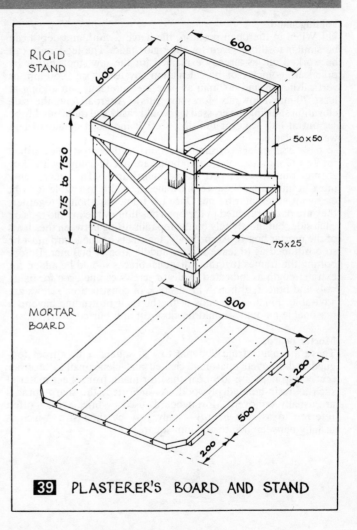

39 PLASTERER'S BOARD AND STAND

Folding stand

40 When in the open position, the height, width and depth can be similar to those given for the rigid stand. The leg-length can be worked out as already explained for the saw stool, either by practical geometry or by calculation (by using, say, 750 mm as vertical height and 600 mm as base measurement and adding at least 70 mm allowance for splay cuts). Alternatively, the side elevation showing the crossed legs could easily and quite quickly be set out at half-scale or full-size, so that the exact details of legs were available.

63 × 38 mm legs (or similar section), with central holes drilled for 9 to 12 mm diameter coach bolts, are fixed together with 75 × 25 mm rails to form two interlocking frames. The inner frame must be minus a tolerance allowance in width to enable it to fit easily into the outer frame. Once the frames are bolted together, they are partly retained in the open position by the middle rails on each side, but mostly rely on the top rails fitting between the cleats of the mortar board. Accordingly, the cleats on the board must be so positioned as to leave a clear middle area of 600 mm. Before bolting the frames together, diagonal braces should be added for extra strength as indicated. Nails or screws can be used for fixing rails and braces, although in this type of construction, screws are advisable. Finally, the ends of the bolts, if protruding beyond a reasonable amount, should be close-cut and burred over.

Mortar boards

These are made from 900 mm to 1 m square, either from tongued-and-grooved boarding, cleated and clench-nailed together (cut, clasp nails are ideal for this), or made from sheet material such as resin-bonded plywood. As indicated, the sharp corners are usually removed. Mortar boards used by bricklayers – often referred to as *spot boards* – only vary by their size, which is usually between 600 to 760 mm square.

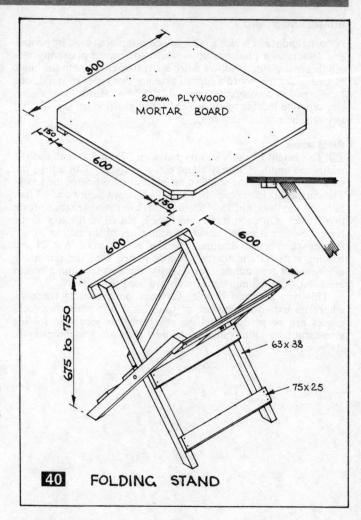

40 FOLDING STAND

BUILDER'S SQUARE

41 Builders' squares are large wooden try-squares, made by the carpenter or joiner, for use on site during the early stages of setting out walls and foundations, etc. Their size varies from about 1 to 2 m and the two blades, forming the square, may be of equal length or have one blade longer than the other. The material, from ex. 75 × 25 mm for the smaller size, up to ex. 125 × 32 mm for the larger squares, should be p.a.r. softwood, carefully selected for density, straight grain and freedom from large knots. A corner half-lap joint is used on the connection of the two blades and should be screwed together. Alternatively, this joint can be formed with a haunched mortice and tenon. Single-splay dovetail halving joints are used to connect the diagonal brace to the blades – and these should also be screwed; joints are not usually glued.

First, make the right-angled corner joint and fix the two blades together temporarily with one screw. Now test for squareness with either a roofing square or by using what is known as the 3–4–5 method. This refers to a ratio of units conforming to Pythagoras's theorem of the square on the hypotenuse being equal to the sum of the squares on the other two sides. For example, using 300 mm as a unit, mark three units (3 × 300 = 900 mm) accurately along one face-side edge from the corner, four units (4 × 300 = 1.2 m) along the adjacent edge from the corner and then check that the diagonal measures five units (5 × 300 = 1.5 m). Adjust the blades, if necessary, until the diagonal measures exactly five units. Lay the brace into position and mark for joints. Dismantle the corner joint, form the other two joints, then reassemble, screw up and test for squareness.

As illustrated, this can be done by laying a straightedge on a flat surface such as a sheet of plywood or hardboard, squaring a mark from this with the builder's square in a left-hand position, reversing the square and marking another line close to the first, and checking for discrepancies in the lines. If necessary, true up any small inaccuracies by planing.

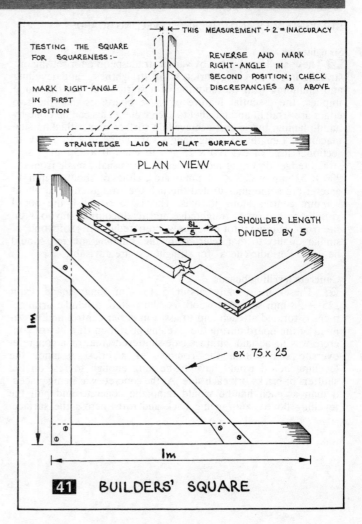

THIS MEASUREMENT ÷ 2 = INACCURACY

TESTING THE SQUARE FOR SQUARENESS :-

REVERSE AND MARK RIGHT-ANGLE IN SECOND POSITION; CHECK DISCREPANCIES AS ABOVE

MARK RIGHT-ANGLE IN FIRST POSITION

STRAIGTEDGE LAID ON FLAT SURFACE

PLAN VIEW

SHOULDER LENGTH DIVIDED BY 5

1m

ex 75 × 25

1m

41 BUILDERS' SQUARE

STRAIGHTEDGES AND CONCRETE LEVELLING BOARDS

Straightedges

42 These are boards used by various tradespeople for setting out straight lines, checking surfaces for straightness, and levelling and plumbing with the addition of a spirit level. As the name implies, the essential feature of these boards is that the two edges are straight and parallel to each other. This can be done by hand-planing, but is best achieved on surface planer/thicknessing machines. Lengths of straightedges vary between 1 to 2 m with sectional sizes of ex. 100 × 25 mm to ex. 150 × 25 mm. Large straightedges of 3 m or more in length, are usually made from ex. 200 × 32 mm or 225 × 38 mm boards. Holes of about 38 mm diameter are sometimes drilled through the straightedge, at about 900 mm centres along its axis. This is to establish the board visually as a proper straightedge and to discourage anybody on site from claiming it for other uses. Prepared (p.a.r.) softwood, of similar quality to that selected for the 'building square', should be used. Periodic checks for straightness are advisable.

Concrete levelling boards

43 These are usually about 5 to 6 m long, made from 225 × 38 mm sawn softwood. As illustrated, a handle arrangement is formed at each end to assist in easier control and movement of the board during the levelling operation. If a bay of concrete was to be laid within a side-shuttered area, or a concrete-oversite slab within the confines of a brick upstand, the levelling board would have to be long enough to rest on the shutters or brickwork each side. As the concrete was being placed, a man at each handle would tamp the concrete and pull the levelling board, zig-zagging back and forth across the surface.

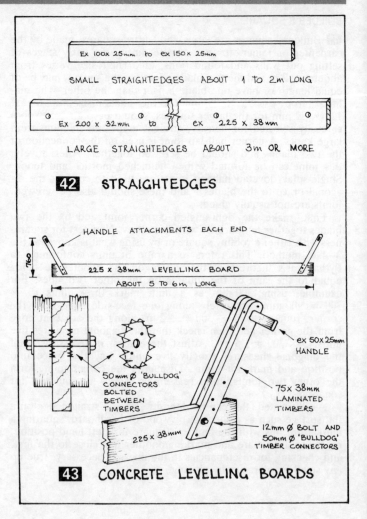

Ex 100 x 25mm to ex 150 x 25mm

SMALL STRAIGHTEDGES ABOUT 1 TO 2m LONG

Ex 200 x 32mm to ex 225 x 38mm

LARGE STRAIGHTEDGES ABOUT 3m OR MORE

42 STRAIGHTEDGES

HANDLE ATTACHMENTS EACH END

225 x 38mm LEVELLING BOARD

ABOUT 5 TO 6m LONG

ex 50 x 25mm HANDLE

75 x 38mm LAMINATED TIMBERS

50mm ∅ 'BULLDOG' CONNECTORS BOLTED BETWEEN TIMBERS

225 x 38mm

12mm ∅ BOLT AND 50mm ∅ 'BULLDOG' TIMBER CONNECTORS

43 CONCRETE LEVELLING BOARDS

PLUMB RULES

Plumb rule

44 This traditional piece of equipment appears to be mostly obsolete nowadays, being replaced by long spirit levels or straightedges with shorter spirit levels placed on their edges. When fixing door linings, or striving for accuracy in plumbing on any similar operation, the straightedge and level combined are preferable to the spirit level on its own.

Plumb rules are usually about 1.650 m long with a sectional size of ex. 125 × 25 mm. Selected p.a.r. softwood is used and the first task is to ensure that the edges are straight and parallel to each other. Then, on the face-side, a gauge line is scored through the centre of the board. Near the bottom, an elliptical or ovoid (egg-shaped) hole is made to accommodate the plumb bob and a wide, wire staple confines its movement to a limited orbit. At the top, three tenon-saw cuts to a depth of about 15 mm are made to hold the plumb-bob string; this simple holding-device allows quick adjustment of the pointed bob if the line stretches and the point does not clear the bottom edge of the cut-out hole. In use, careful positioning of the plumb rule is required to promote a gentle bobbing of the bob and line against the gauge line. Having achieved this, visual checking at the base of the line indicates plumbness or out-of-plumb, according to how the string line and point of bob relates to the gauge line.

The main advantage that a plumb rule (or straightedge-level) has over a spirit-level on its own, say in relation to plumbing and fixing door linings, is that, apart from plumbness, any hollows or rounds in the surface of the partially-fixed lining, show up easily because of the plumb rule or straightedge's length.

Battering plumb rule

45 This is similar to the above, except that it is wide at the top and narrow at the bottom, one side being parallel to the central gauge line, the other tapered down. It is used on walls being built with a battered (inclined) face, such as retaining walls, tall factory chimneys and buttresses. Providing the correct angle – set up by degrees or to a given ratio – is formed on the tapered side of the board, plumb readings will ensure a true progressive incline. As indicated, a spirit level can replace the use of the plumb bob.

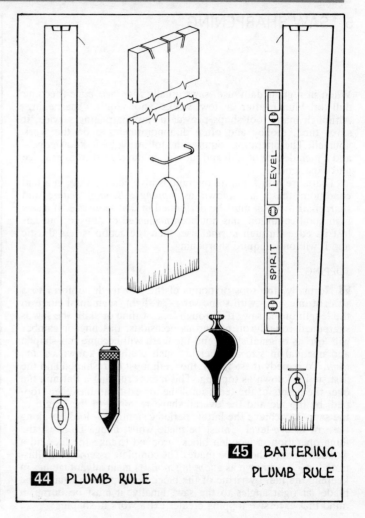

44 PLUMB RULE

45 BATTERING PLUMB RULE

5 SAW SHARPENING

When in regular daily use, saws usually *lose their edge* (become dull or blunt) after a few weeks and require sharpening. Although many tool shops provide a saw-sharpening service, it saves time, money and often disappointment to do the work yourself. The operation requires the following basic knowledge – and a high degree of skill and judgement developed from practice and experience.

There are four separate operations involved for saws in a bad condition; these are known as *topping, shaping, setting* and *sharpening* – which must be performed in that sequence. If a saw is in good condition, has not been neglected or abused, but has lost its edge through normal use, then the action is less drastic and it will only require sharpening.

TOPPING

1 Normally, the tops or points of the saw teeth conform to a straight line, or – with some saws – a slight, segmental curve in the length of the saw. If, through lack of time or skill, the saw is sharpened roughly on numerous occasions, this line or camber will lose its original shape and the teeth will become mis-shapen and unequal in size and height. Such teeth are known as *dog teeth*. To remedy these faults, the teeth must be reshaped and the first step is known as topping. This means running a flat mill file over the points of the teeth until the lowest tooth has been 'topped' by the file and the overall shape regained in the length of the saw. To achieve the latter, periodic sightings – looking along the saw at eye-level – must be made whilst filing. To assist the filing operation, a wooden block, grooved to take the file and a wooden wedge, should be made. The complete assembly, as illustrated at ⓒ, is known as a *topping tool*. Its main advantage lies in keeping the file, by virtue of the block being pressed against the blade, at right angles to the saw. Finally, it must be borne in mind that excessive topping creates extra work in shaping.

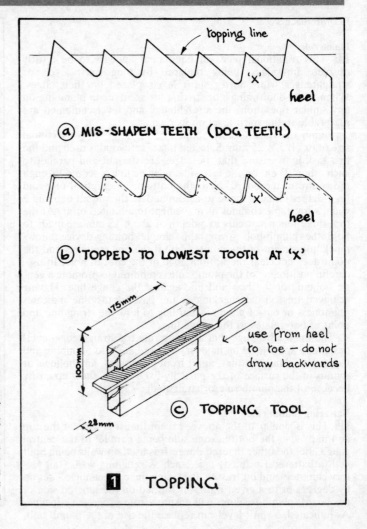

ⓐ MIS-SHAPEN TEETH (DOG TEETH)

ⓑ 'TOPPED' TO LOWEST TOOTH AT 'X'

ⓒ TOPPING TOOL

175mm
100mm
28mm
use from heel to toe – do not draw backwards

1 TOPPING

SHAPING

2 This operation is carried out with a saw file. Such files are equilaterally triangular (60°), slim-tapered in various lengths, single- or double-ended and fitted into plastic or wooden saw-file handles. A 150 mm double-ended file is recommended for tenon and panel saws and a 200 or 225 mm double-ended file for crosscut and rip saws. When shaping, the filing action is always square across the saw blade and follows in every consecutive gullet from the heel on the left to the toe on the right. The idea is to eliminate the 'dog teeth' and create evenly shaped teeth leaning towards the toe of the saw at the correct 'pitch' and points per 25 mm. Pitch refers to the angle-of-lean given to the front cutting edges of the teeth, as shown in Chapter 2. The recommended pitch angle for rip saws is 87°, crosscut saws, 80°, panel and tenon saws, 75°. Until experience is gained, the required pitch angle can be set on a metal template or sliding bevel to test the degree of accuracy in initial shaping.

When filing, the handle should be held firmly in one hand and the end of the file steadied with the thumb and first two fingers of the other hand. All file strokes should be forward-acting and *not* drawn backwards. Take care to establish the correct angles on the first few teeth and then familiarize yourself with the 'feel' of the file resting in a corrected gullet; maintain this 'feel' as you continue the shaping operation and combine it with visual appraisal of the shape and pitch of the teeth in relation to the shiny, flat spots on the tips – produced in the topping operation – which will gradually diminish as the gullets deepen and will indicate that the shaping must stop immediately the shiny flat spots are removed. Some tradespeople rub chalk on the file periodically to reduce the tendency of the file to become clogged with metal particles.

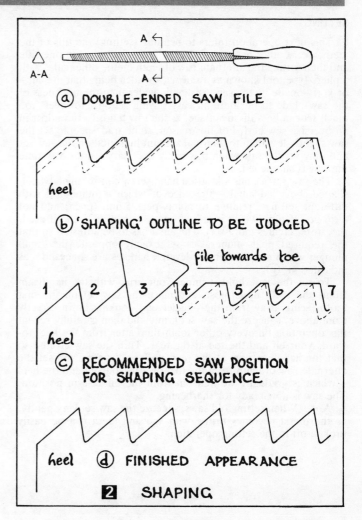

(a) DOUBLE-ENDED SAW FILE

(b) 'SHAPING' OUTLINE TO BE JUDGED

file towards toe

(c) RECOMMENDED SAW POSITION FOR SHAPING SEQUENCE

(d) FINISHED APPEARANCE

2 SHAPING

SETTING

3 This next operation refers to bending (setting) the tips of the teeth, every other one, out from the face of the saw on one side and then setting the alternate row of teeth on the other side, with a pliers-type tool known as a *saw set*, the idea being that the cut – or kerf – made by the saw, is slightly wider than the thickness of the saw blade to facilitate an easy sawing action. However, too much *set* can be a disadvantage, as the saw tends to run adrift in an oversize saw kerf. For this reason, some tradespeople set the saw slightly less than the normal amount indicated on the saw set and only set the saw when it is really necessary – not every time the saw is sharpened.

The saw set ⓐ, has a knurled hand-screw controlling a wheel-shaped, bevelled anvil – the edge of which is numbered with different settings, relative to points per 25 mm (pp25) and not *teeth* per 25 mm (which is always one less than pp25 and if used, therefore, creates more set). The anvil has to be adjusted so that the required pp25 numeral is set exactly opposite the small plunger which ejects when the levered handles are squeezed – as indicated at ⓑ .

To set the saw, hold it under your arm, with the handle in front, the teeth uppermost, and place the saw set on the first tooth facing away from the plunger and, looking down directly from above, squeeze the saw set firmly and then carefully repeat this operation on every other tooth thereafter from the heel towards yourself and the toe at the rear. Turn the saw around so that the handle is now at the rear, under your arm, and set the alternate row of teeth from the toe towards yourself and the heel – which is gradually worked out from the under-arm position. The saw is now ready for sharpening.

Note: When setting old saws, squeeze the saw set very gently, as the metal becomes brittle with age and teeth can be easily broken off in the setting operation.

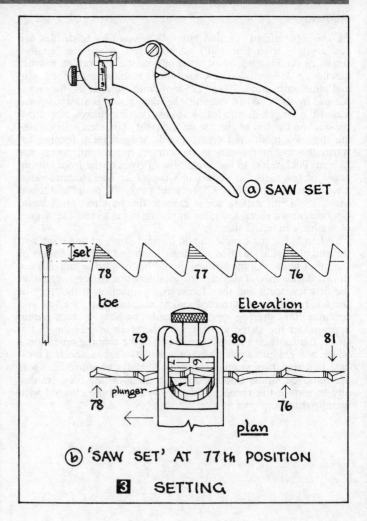

ⓐ SAW SET

set

78   77   76

toe   Elevation

79   80   81

plunger

78   76

plan

ⓑ 'SAW SET' AT 77th POSITION

3   SETTING

SHARPENING

4 This final operation is concerned with creating sharp edges and points to the outer tips of the teeth, by filing every other gullet at an angle to the face of the saw on one side and then the alternate row of gullets at an opposing angle to the face of the saw on the other side – ⓑ. This method of sharpening is for saws designed to cut across the grain, such as crosscut, panel and tenon saws, the theory being that the sharp pointed outer tips of the vee-shaped teeth act as knives cutting two close lines across the timber. Short-grained pieces of fibre between the lines break up as the saw moves forward; the broken fibres are collected in the gullets as *sawdust* and released when the saw passes through the timber. Rip saws are similarly sharpened on alternate sides, but the angle of sharpening is square or almost square across the saw ⓐ. This eliminates the pointed outer tips required for cross-cutting and produces square-tipped teeth which provide a scraping/shearing action necessary for effective down-grain ripping.

When sharpening, take care not to lose the basic shape of the teeth; this is best achieved by gaining the 'feel' of the file and by keeping your eye on the back edges of the teeth. The first stroke of the saw file, at an angle of 60° to 70° to the saw face, should show a parallel chamfer on the back edge of the tooth – if not parallel, then adjust the file accordingly on subsequent strokes and stop filing immediately the chamfer-edged tooth becomes completely bevel-edged – ⓒ. This normally takes from two to four strokes and once established, each gullet should receive the same number of strokes thereafter. This promotes a rhythmic filing-action necessary for speed and accuracy. If a saw is only being resharpened, whereby the edges of the teeth are already bevelled, it helps to 'top' the saw lightly – repeat *lightly* – with the topping tool. The idea is to split the shiny flat spots in half when sharpening from one side and then remove the remaining halves when sharpening from the other side.

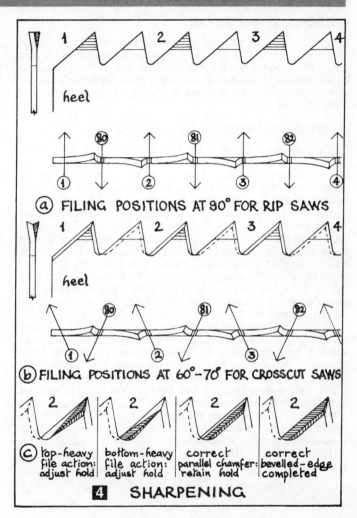

ⓐ FILING POSITIONS AT 90° FOR RIP SAWS

ⓑ FILING POSITIONS AT 60°–70° FOR CROSSCUT SAWS

ⓒ top-heavy file action: adjust hold | bottom-heavy file action: adjust hold | correct parallel chamfer: retain hold | correct bevelled-edge completed

4 SHARPENING

SAW HORSES OR SAW STOCKS

5 Special vices can be used for saw sharpening, but more commonly wooden frames known as *saw horses* or *saw stocks* are used. The wooden jaws which hold the saw in the frame are known as *saw chops*. Saw horses are purpose-made and the design and construction is shown in the chapter dealing with making small plant on site.

SHARPENING PROCEDURE (for right-handed persons)

6 (a) Cramp the saw high in the saw chops and 'top' lightly with the topping tool. (b) Reposition the saw so that only about 4 mm remains between the top of the saw chops and the base of the gullets. With the saw handle to your left, rest the saw horse against a bench or window-cill, etc. with a good light in front and above the saw. (c) Take up your position against the horse by resting your right foot on the bottom rail, with your knee pressing against the top rail to keep the saw horse steady. (d) Start to file at the heel (near the saw handle), in the gullet affecting the back of the first tooth leaning away – noting that the file, at an angle of 60° to 70°, *always points towards the saw handle*. After two or three forward strokes, aimed at 'splitting the shiner', repeat the action in every other gullet thereafter, moving rhythmically towards the toe of the saw on your right.

When the last quarter of the saw's length is reached, it will be found easier to switch the leg position and support the horse with the left foot and knee. (e) When completed, turn the horse around so that the saw handle is now to your right. Support the horse with the left foot and knee and start to file at the heel again (near the handle), in the gullet affecting the back of the first tooth leaning away, remembering that the file *always points towards the saw handle*. With the same amount of file strokes used on the first operation, aim to remove the remaining 'shiner' and produce sharp points whilst moving rhythmically towards the toe of the saw on your left – (e). In the last quarter, switch the leg position to give support with the right foot and knee.

1 = saw chops
2 = top (knee) rail
3 = bottom (foot) rail

SAW HORSE 5

(a) **TOPPING POSITION**

(b) **SHARPENING POSITION**

(c)

(d) START FILING → FINISH
STAND HERE → → → → STAND HERE

(e) FINISH ← START FILING
STAND HERE ← ← ← ← STAND HERE

6 SHARPENING PROCEDURE

6 FIXING DOOR FRAMES AND LININGS

Wooden frames and linings are fixed within wall or screen openings to accommodate doors which are to be hung at a later stage in the second-fixing operation. This arrangement is necessary where 'wet trades' (bricklaying and plastering) are involved. Where dry methods of construction are used, or achieved (as described in **23** and **24**), *doorsets* are sometimes specified. These comprise linings or frames with pre-hung doors attached, locks or latches and architraves in position. This reduces site work by eliminating the conventional second-fixing door-hanging operation. **1** A door lining – by definition – should completely cover the reveals (sides) and soffit (underside of lintel) of an opening, as well as support and house the door.

2 A door frame should be strong enough to support and house the door without relying completely on the fixings to the structural opening. Unlike linings, frames do not usually cover the entire width of reveals or soffit – except when used within internal partition walls.

Generally speaking, frames are used for external entrance doors, and linings for internal doors. Apart from this, door frames are usually set up and built in at the time the opening is being formed, whereas a lining, because of its thinness (21 to 28 mm) and flexibility, should only be fixed after the opening is formed. It also requires a greater number of fixings and a more involved fixing technique than a door frame (see **14a** to **14p**)
3 (a) To inhibit excessive moisture penetration into the timber from wet trades, built-in frames should be primed or treated with preservative – and may have a continuous strip of damp-proof material such as bituminous felt, plastic film (to BS 743) or waterproof building paper fixed to the outside edges and top. (b) and (c) show the use of plastic film fixed to jambs and sandwiched between brickwork and blockwork to stop any moisture in the outer skin (wall) from bridging the cavity.

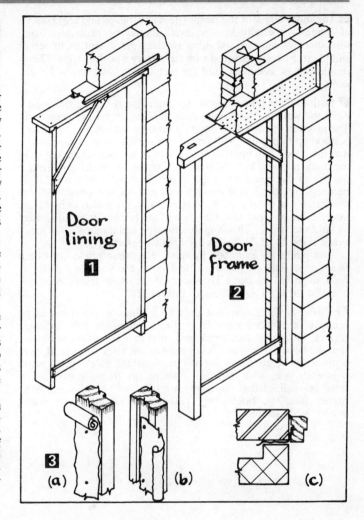

Door lining **1**

Door frame **2**

3 (a)   (b)   (c)

4 The inner edges of the jambs (sides) of frames and legs (sides) of linings, especially at low level, should be protected from wheelbarrow damage and other careless movement of material and plant, by being covered with temporary wooden strips. These should not be removed until the wet trades have finished their work.

5 Built-in door frames are set up immediately before starting to build the walls, or sometimes after the first course has been laid. The position of each door-opening reveal is set out and the frame is stood up in position with one or two scaffold boards supporting it at the head. Two boards (or two nails in one board) are better if the frame happens to be twisted. A 75 mm wire nail driven through the top of the board holds the frame. The nail is driven through before lifting the board into position and the nail-point rests on the frame – is not driven in. Alternatively, the nail is only driven *into* the board – not through it – and the head of the nail is used to hold the frame. This is quite effective and a much safer practice if removal of the nail is eventually neglected.

The jambs are plumbed by spirit level, then bricks (or other heavy material) are piled at the foot of the scaffold boards to hold them in position. The head of the door frame must be checked for level and adjusted if necessary.

6 These adjustments must only be minimal if the frame is to relate to a finished floor level (f.f.l.), although, with external frames, up against face brickwork, it is also important to ensure that the head of the frame is adjusted to suit brick courses. If, say, a precast-concrete plank lintel is to be bedded on the brick bearings each side, with its soffit touching the frame-head, then it must be realized that the frame must be one bed-joint (10 mm) higher than the brick-gauge (predetermined height of brickwork), as illustrated.

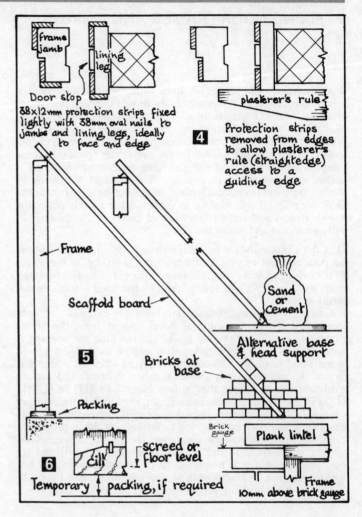

Door stop
38×12mm protection strips fixed lightly with 38mm oval nails to jambs and lining legs, ideally to face and edge

plasterer's rule

4 Protection strips removed from edges to allow plasterer's rule (straightedge) access to a guiding edge

Frame

Scaffold board

5

Bricks at base

Sand or cement

Alternative base & head support

Packing

6 Temporary ↕ packing, if required

screed or floor level

Cill

Brick gauge

Plank lintel

Frame 10mm above brick gauge

FIXING TIES

7 As the brickwork or blockwork proceeds, metal ties are fixed to the jambs and built in to the bed joints. The first set of ties (one to each jamb) must be fixed at low level: on the first course of blockwork, or on the second or third course of brickwork – no higher.

As the work progresses, the frame must be checked for plumbness from time to time in case the supporting scaffold boards have been accidentally knocked. At least two more sets of ties are fixed, at middle and near-top positions. For storey-height frames (from floor to ceiling, with fixed glass or fanlight above door opening), a total of four sets of ties is advisable.

Different types of tie are available, each with various points for and against, as listed below:

Galvanized steel frame cramps

7a These provide good fixings and because they are screwed to the frame, any cramps (or ties) already fixed and bedded in mortar are not disturbed by hammering; by resting on the last-laid brick, the next brick above the tie is easily bedded. Disadvantages are: handling small screws; requiring a screwdriver and bradawl (if no carpenters are on site in the early stages of the contract); if no groove is in the frame, the upturned end of the cramp inhibits the next brick from touching the frame; doubts as to whether rust-proofed screws were used.

Owlett's zinc-plated screw ties

7b These also provide good fixings, and are screwed to the frame without vibration from hammering. They do not require screws, bradawl or screwdriver and can be offset or skewed to avoid cavities. On the debit side, the brickwork has to be stopped one course below the required fixing to allow rotation of the loop when screwing in, then the brick beneath the tie is bedded – with some difficulty.

Sherardized Holdfasts

7c Holdfasts are fixed quickly and easily, being driven in by hammer. The spiked ends spread outwards when driven into the wood, forming a fishtail. The main disadvantage is that the hammering disturbs the frame and permanently loosens any Holdfasts already positioned in the still-green mortar.

Whatever type of frame cramps or ties are used, their intended positions, relative to bed-joints, are best marked on the jambs boldly with a soft pencil (as seen in **7** at (1), (2) and (3)), to act as a reminder to the bricklayer as the work rises.

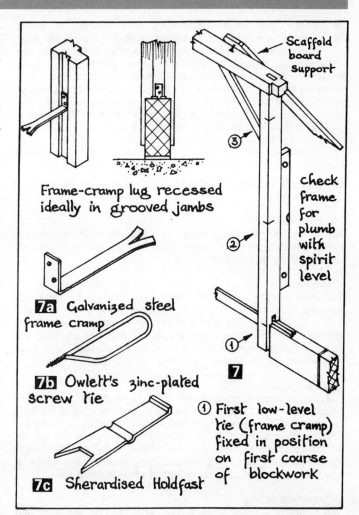

Frame-cramp lug recessed ideally in grooved jambs

7a Galvanized steel frame cramp

7b Owlett's zinc-plated screw tie

7c Sherardised Holdfast

Scaffold board support

check frame for plumb with spirit level

7

(1) First low-level tie (frame cramp) fixed in position on first course of blockwork

8 Usually, one or two strips of sawn timber, of about 18 × 50 mm section, acting as temporary diagonal corner braces, are nailed lightly to the frame to keep it square at the head, and another piece, called a *stretcher*, is fixed near the bottom to keep the jambs set apart at the correct width. Although there is a tendency on site to remove these at the outset because they obstruct easy passage through the opening, they should not be knocked or removed until the surrounding *green* (new) brick or blockwork is set. **8a** indicates gaps at the sides of a frame cramp which will cause lateral looseness of the frame. This is due to the frame being knocked or the braces and stretcher being removed (knocked off) too early, before the mortar was set.

9 Although not often used nowadays, other methods of fixing frames included:

Cut clasp nails
9a 75 or 100 mm long, these are driven dovetail-fashion, for about one-third of their length, into the back of the frame and bedded in the mortar joint.

Wooden pallets
9b Also called pads, these were usually made from softwood, although elm was considered best, prepared to a size of about 100 × 75 × 9 mm and built into the bed joints each side of the opening, for fixing the frame (or lining) after the opening was formed. The pads were always positioned so that the end grain was *not* on the fixing side.

Axed plugs
9c Again usually made from softwood, these were propeller-shaped by the axe and driven into bed joints which had been cut out by using a plugging chisel and hammer after the opening was formed. When driven in, the propeller-shaped plugs twisted and set up reactions to offset eventual timber shrinkage. Bearing in mind that this type of plug presented an inferior end-grain fixing, the best proven fixings were achieved with cut clasp nails.

Fibre or plastic plugs
9d Nowadays, if the frame is fixed after the opening is formed, fixings may be achieved by drilling, plugging and screwing with fibre or plastic plugs.

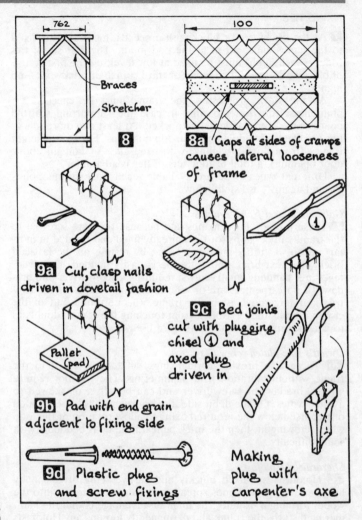

762

Braces

Stretcher

8

100

8a Gaps at sides of cramps causes lateral looseness of frame

9a Cut clasp nails driven in dovetail fashion

①

Pallet (pad)

9b Pad with end grain adjacent to fixing side

9c Bed joints cut with plugging chisel ① and axed plug driven in

9d Plastic plug and screw fixings

Making plug with carpenter's axe

FRAME DETAILS

10 For purposes of weathering and structural transition between exterior/interior levels and finish, external door frames usually have hardwood cills – sometimes called thresholds. Water bars, with a sectional size of 25 × 6 mm, run along a groove in the top of the cill, protruding 12 mm to form a water check/draught excluder. These bars can be brass, galvanized steel or plastic-sheathed steel. Both cill and water bar must withstand wear and tear from foot traffic and weather exposure.

11 Cills also provide excellent anchorage for the feet of the jambs which are tenoned into them, as at **11a** . Although usually through-morticed, the softwood jambs would be better protected if only stub-tenoned into the hardwood cill. If the frame is of the type without a cill, 18 mm diameter metal dowels can be used to secure the jambs, as at **11b** . With brace and 18 mm diameter Jennings' twist bit, a hole is drilled up into the foot of each jamb and the dowels are hammered in to leave a 40 to 50 mm protrusion. When the frame is being set up, the protruding dowels are either set into dowel holes or are bedded in concrete, or sand and cement floor screed, etc. Galvanized steel pipe, of a suitable diameter, is frequently used for dowels.

12 External frames should be ⓐ rebated from solid wood to house the door, but internal types may have ⓑ separate door-stops fixed to the jambs and underside of head to form a rebate. The former is referred to as *sunken* or *stuck* rebates and the latter as *loose* or *planted* door stops.

13 The horns on the head and/or cill should not be cut off, as they add strength to the mortice and tenon joints and are normally built into the brickwork to help support the frame. However, if the frame is to be flush with the brickwork on one side or only marginally set back, some part of the horn should be removed, as shown in the isometric views at ⓐ, ⓑ and ⓒ. ⓓ shows the possible effect of jamb displacement if the horn is completely removed.

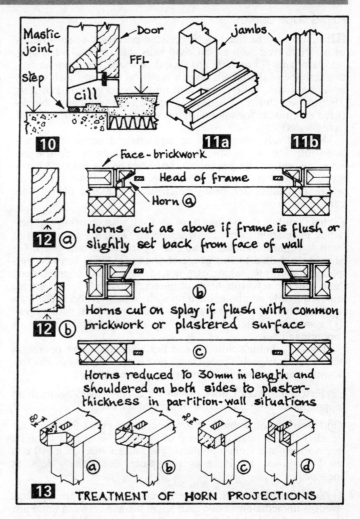

Horns cut as above if frame is flush or slightly set back from face of wall

Horns cut on splay if flush with common brickwork or plastered surface

Horns reduced to 30mm in length and shouldered on both sides to plaster-thickness in partition-wall situations

13 TREATMENT OF HORN PROJECTIONS

FIXING DOOR LININGS

14 Linings may be fixed to timber stud partitions or sub-frames with 75 mm oval nails or cut clasp nails, but on solid walls only cut clasp nails (75 or 100 mm) should be used. The squarish sectional shape of these nails takes a very firm grip into such fixings as timber plugs, pallets (pads), or into aerated materials such as Thermalite, Durox, Tacbloc, Lignacite, etc. insulation blocks (used extensively for solid partition walling and the inner skin of cavity walls).

Alternatively, linings may be counterbored, screwed and pelleted into fibre or plastic plugs, pads, grounds or sub frames; screwing and pelleting is usually restricted to the fixing of hardwood linings, but can be justified on good-class softwood jobs, or where difficulties are being experienced with nail fixings into certain materials.

(a) to (f) outline the various steps involved with screwing and pelleting in relation to the following notes: (a) lining counterbored with a 12 mm diameter centre or twist bit, 10 mm deep; (b) shankhole drilled to suit gauge of screw; (c) lining screwed into plugged wall, etc. taking care not to damage the counterbored hole with the revolving blade of the screwdriver; (d) pellet glued, entered lightly into hole, lined up with grain direction and driven in carefully; (e) bulk of surplus pellet removed with chisel; (f) remaining pellet cleaned off flush with a block plane or smoothing plane.

Due to a lining's thinness and flexibility, the fixing operation can be unmanageable unless a set procedure is adopted. The following fixing technique, therefore, is recommended:

(g) First remove door stops, which are usually nailed lightly in an approximate position on the lining, and set aside.

(h) If working on unfinished concrete floors, check finished floor level (f.f.l.) in relation to base of linings. This is best done by measuring down from a predetermined datum line set at 900 mm or 1 m above f.f.l. Place packing pieces under lining legs, as necessary.

(i) Stabilize the lining in an approximate position by placing small wedges immediately above each leg in the gap between lintel and head – and then check the head with a spirit level. If gaps exist, as is usual, between the structural opening and the back of the lining's legs, pack out with pieces of non-splitting material such

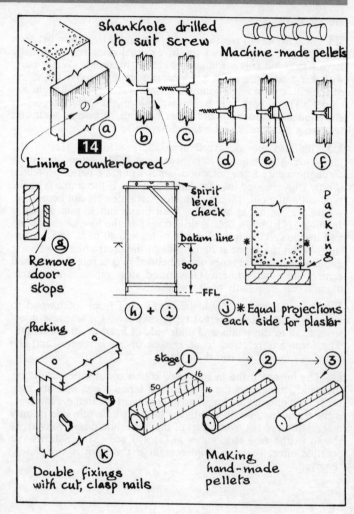

Shankhole drilled to suit screw

Machine-made pellets

14 Lining counterbored

(a) (b) (c) (d) (e) (f)

Remove door stops (g)

Spirit level check

Datum line

900

FFL

(h) + (i)

Packing

J * Equal projections each side for plaster

Packing

stage (1) → (2) → (3)

50   16   16

Double fixings with cut, clasp nails (k)

Making hand-made pellets

as hardboard or plywood, initially on each side of the top fixing positions only.

(j) Adjust top of lining to establish equal projections each side of the opening for eventual plastering of wall surfaces.

(k) Fix lining at top, *through* packings on each leg, with two nails per fixing.

(l) Plumb the lining on the face side and edge with a long spirit level or a plumb rule (alternatively, use a spirit level placed on a straightedge). Pack the bottom position each side as required and fix through one packing only. Check squareness of fixed leg at the base with straightedge and try-square, as illustrated, then pack and complete the intermediate fixings on the same leg, checking before and after each fixing with plumb rule or straightedge. The amount of fixing points on each side should be ideally five, but not less than four, i.e. near-top, near-bottom, and two or three intermediate points on each side.

(m) Next, remove stretcher from base of frame, hold it up to a position just below lining head, mark exact inside-lining width and cut to make a 'pinch rod'.

(n) Fit pinch rod in bottom section of linings and pack accordingly behind lower fixing point on unfixed leg.

(o) Check plumbness of leg for correct sideways position and check alignment by sighting across the face edges as illustrated. Fix bottom, then intermediate positions, moving pinch rod to each fixing area and packing out before fixing. The lining head will only require fixing to the lintel if the opening exceeds normal width.

(p) However, wedges or packing should be driven into any gap between lintel and head, at the two extremes immediately above each leg. Failure to complete this detail can result in the head becoming partially disjointed from the legs (at the tongued-housing joint) when final nailing of the head door-stop is completed at a later stage.

Remove corner brace(s) (although this could have been done earlier, after (h), to facilitate easier working), punch in all nail fixings to about 3 mm below the surface – or, if screwed, complete the pelleting operation as outlined in (d) to (f).

Finally, replace door stops and fix protection strips to lower face edges, if considered necessary.

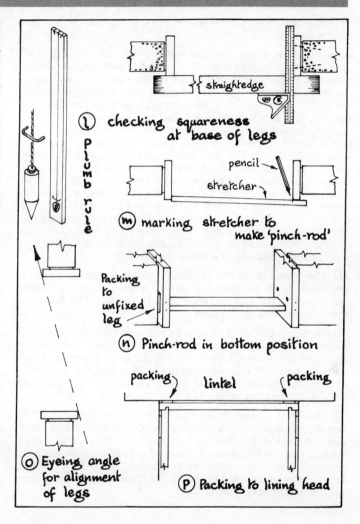

(l) checking squareness at base of legs

plumb rule

pencil
stretcher

(m) marking stretcher to make 'pinch-rod'

Packing to unfixed leg

(n) Pinch-rod in bottom position

packing   lintel   packing

(o) Eyeing angle for alignment of legs

(P) Packing to lining head

SETTING UP INTERNAL FRAMES PRIOR TO BUILDING BLOCK-PARTITIONS

15 In these situations, the first step is to set out the wall positions on the concrete floor in accordance with the architect's drawings. Providing the structural walls are square to each other, the various internal partitions required need only be measured out at two extreme points from any wall to form parallels and squares. This is best done with a steel tape rule and a method of marking known as *spotting*; a spot of mortar (about half a trowelful) is placed in position on the floor, then trowelled down to form a thin slither. The tape rule, preferably being held at one end, is pulled taut over the mortar spot and the trowel-tip is cut through the mortar at the required measurement. Short offset walls can be set out by using a builder's square (a wooden square, the making of which is covered in Chapter 4). Once the position of all the walls is determined, the next step is to set out the required door openings. Straightedges can be used to join extreme marks and so allow further spots to be placed at intermediate positions to indicate the openings.

16 The frames should be stood up to relate to the setting out – preferably when the mortar is set – and some means of holding the frames at the foot and head must be devised. The following optional methods can be used.

(a) The first course of blocks can be laid and when set will act as a means of steadying the feet in one direction, whilst loose blocks on either side will hold the position in the other direction. Alternatively, notched pieces of wood can be placed against the feet or against the protruding metal dowels on the opening side and fixed to the floor by means of a cartridge tool.

(b) The head of each frame can be held by a leaning scaffold board or boards – but a far better method is to use wall cleats and a system of top braces. The braces, ex. 50 × 18 mm sawn timber, must be triangulated or placed in such a way as to create stability. The wall cleats, approximately 100 × 25 × 300 mm long, are normally fixed to the walls with cut clasp nails – heads protruding for easy removal later.

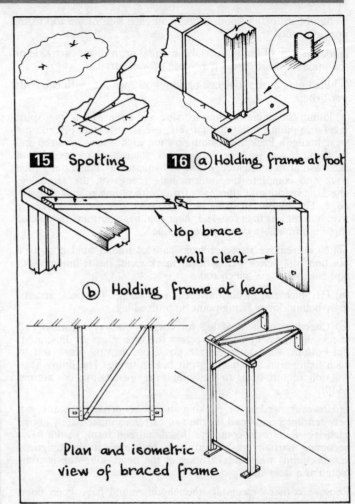

15 Spotting

16 (a) Holding frame at foot

top brace

wall cleat

(b) Holding frame at head

Plan and isometric view of braced frame

STOREY FRAMES

17 Storey frames may be internal or external and, as the name implies, fully occupy the vertical space between floor and ceiling. The frame comprises two extended jambs, a head, a transom above the door and usually a hardwood cill on external types. The frame-space above the door can be (a) directly glazed, (b) contain louvres, (c) house a fixed sash, or (d) an opening sash (fanlight) for ventilation.

18 Another type of storey frame sometimes used on block partitions less than 100 mm thick, may be minus the fanlight aperture, but have extended jambs to allow for some form of fixing to the ceiling. This gives greater rigidity to the thinner wall whose strength would otherwise be impaired by the introduction of an opening. The jambs protruding above head level should be reduced by the plaster thickness on each outer edge and, after the wall is built, these edges should be covered with a strip of expanded metal lath unless dry-lining methods are to be used. When the ceiling above the storey frame is timber-joisted, the extended jambs are fixed to the sides of the joists or – more likely – to purpose-placed noggings between the joists. When the construction is of concrete, a timber batten or ground can be 'shot' onto the ceiling with a cartridge tool and the jamb-ends fixed to this by (a) notching (cogging) or (b) butting and skew-nailing.

SUB FRAMES

19 These can be recessed to take insulation blocks, hollow clay pots or concrete-block partitions. The recess helps to stabilize the wall during construction and the sub frame provides an eventual means of fixing the lining and architraves. Sub frames are advisable when there is likely to be a fixing problem, as with concrete blocks or pot walls in relation to linings – particularly hardwood linings – being fixed after the walls are constructed. When being built in, recessed frames must receive metal ties or frame cramps as normal – and may be used as (a) sub frames to receive linings or (b) frames in themselves.

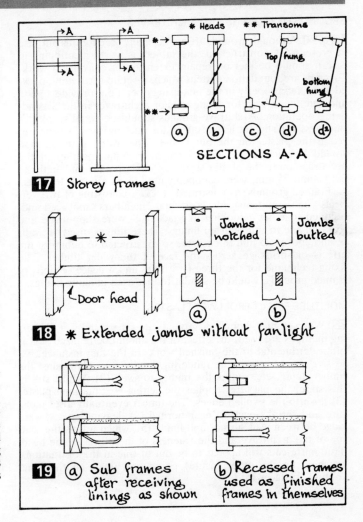

17 Storey frames

Sections A-A

18 ✳ Extended jambs without fanlight

19 (a) Sub frames after receiving linings as shown

(b) Recessed frames used as finished frames in themselves

GROUNDS FOR LININGS AND ARCHITRAVES

20 & **21** Although grounds are not normally used for this purpose in present-day construction, the subject is worth mentioning in case it should be met on repair, extension or conversion work. Grounds are foundation battens which, if set up accurately, packed and fixed properly in the first-fixing operation, provide a good and true fixing base for linings and/or architraves in the second-fixing operation. Architrave-grounds should be equal to plaster thickness (or slightly less to allow for packing) and bevelled to retain the plaster on the outer edge. The width of the ground should be such as to allow a minimum 6 mm overlap of the architrave on to the plaster surface. Cut clasp nails, in lengths of 50, 63 and 75 mm, were commonly used to fix grounds to walls.

Framed grounds, as illustrated at **20** , consisting of two verticals and multi-spaced horizontal members morticed-and-tenoned together – looking like ladders – were shop-made and fixed on site to suit built-up linings. These linings, used on walls of and above 225 mm thick, were so constructed to minimize the effects of shrinkage across the face of the wider timber. The fixing technique for the three (two sides and a head) sections of framed grounds, would be similar to that used in fixing linings.

MOISTURE EFFECT FROM WET PLASTER

22 When frames, linings or grounds are set up and wet plastering methods are used, the effect of this should be realized as it is often detrimental to the finished work. In the first instance, excessive moisture from the rendering/floating coat (1) against the timber lining, etc. causes the timber to swell (2). Whilst still in this state, the plasterer applies the setting coat/finishing plaster (3) flush to the swollen edges. The timber eventually loses moisture and shrinks back to near normal (4), leaving an awkward ridge between wall surface and lining (5), which upsets the seating of the architrave and the trueness of the mitres at the head. True mitre-cuts will appear to be out of true in these situations, touching on the outer (acute) points and open on the inner (obtuse) surfaces (6).

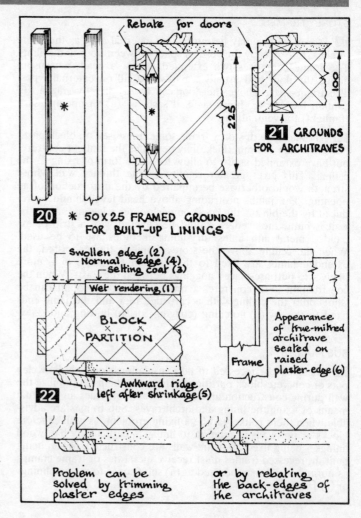

Rebate for doors

21 GROUNDS FOR ARCHITRAVES

20 * 50×25 FRAMED GROUNDS FOR BUILT-UP LININGS

Swollen edge (2)
Normal edge (4)
Setting coat (3)
Wet rendering (1)
BLOCK PARTITION
Awkward ridge left after shrinkage (5)

Appearance of true-mitred architrave seated on raised plaster-edge (6)
Frame

22

Problem can be solved by trimming plaster edges

or by rebating the back-edges of the architraves

DOORSETS

23 As mentioned earlier, these comprise linings or frames with pre-hung doors attached, locks or latches and one or two sets of architraves in position. These units are supplied by specialist firms producing doorsets as a factory operation. The main advantage of this relatively modern innovation is a reduction in time-consuming site work by eliminating conventional door-hanging, architrave and lock-fitting and fixing.

Because doorsets are complete units, they are not immediately suitable where conventional methods of construction, involving 'wet trades', are to be used. The issues against this practice include architrave and hinge protrusion, which inhibits conventional plastering methods, greater risk of damage to doors and possible distortion of door-jointing tolerances due to moisture attraction from wet plaster causing swelling.

24 The alternatives, therefore, are: (a) fixing linings and frames by conventional methods in conventional situations where 'wet trades' are involved, as already covered by **1** to **14** of this chapter (b) avoiding the use of 'wet trades' and using doorsets, or (c) modifying the 'wet trade' operation to enable the use of doorsets.

24b This situation is achieved when *dry-lining* methods are used. These methods produce finished wall surfaces without using wet plaster. One particular method uses tapered-edge sheets of plasterboard which are pressed into position against fibre-board pads and dabs of plaster placed at recommended spacings on the structural wall. The joints are finally taped and filled to a flush finish.

24c The modification mentioned above involves producing plywood profiles (minimum 12 mm thick), cut to *finished* wall thickness and fixed around the door opening like a traditional lining, either temporarily as a guide for the wet plaster, or permanently as an initial guide for plaster and a subsequent sub frame for doorset fixings.

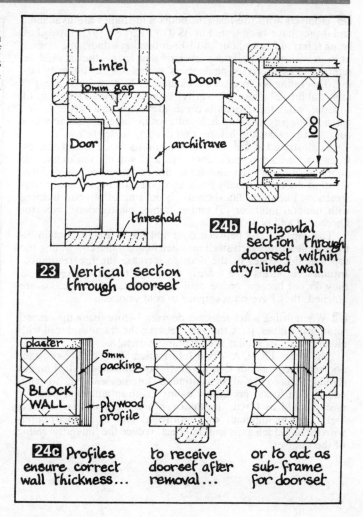

23 Vertical section through doorset

24b Horizontal section through doorset within dry-lined wall

24c Profiles ensure correct wall thickness... to receive doorset after removal... or to act as sub-frame for doorset

25 Doorsets with fire-resistant doors and frames are available, and if they have been tested to BS 476 : Part 8 : 1972, instead of being referred to as ½-hour and 1-hour firecheck doors and frames as in previous years – under less stringent tests – they should be referred to as 'fire resisting doorsets' with a stability/integrity rating. This rating is expressed in minutes, as 30/30 or 30/20, etc. (30 min. stability/20 minutes integrity). *Stability* refers to the point of collapse, when the doorset becomes ineffective as a barrier to fire spread. *Integrity* refers to holes or gaps in the construction when cold, or to cracks and fissures that develop under test.

As illustrated at **25** , fire resisting doorsets are identifiable by frames with 25 mm thick doorstops and varying thicknesses of door, according to the amount of fire resistance required. Fire-resistant doors are usually made up of: (1) solid-core timber construction, like thick blockboard; (2) built up of ply-clad framing with mineral infill; or (3) timber frame, plasterboard, asbestos fibreboard and plywood facings.

The gaps (joints) between door and frame usually contain intumescent strips which swell up when heated, thereby sealing the top and side edges of the door to increase the fire resistance. Intumescent strips give a fairly good seal to hot smoke, but as they do not become active until temperatures of 200–250°C are reached, they have no resistance to cold smoke.

26 When fitting a fire-resistant doorset, before fixing the second set of architraves, pack the gaps between the frame and wall with mineral wool or similar fire-resistant material.

The latest TRADA Wood Information Sheet on fire-resistant doorsets recommends that narrow – not broadleaf – steel hinges should be used, to allow continuous intumescent-strip to jamb edges; slim locks, preferably painted with intumescent paint or paste should be fitted; the thickness and thermal mass of these locks must be minimal; 'over-morticing' must be avoided, otherwise these hidden gaps will, in effect, reduce the 'integrity' rating of the doorset.

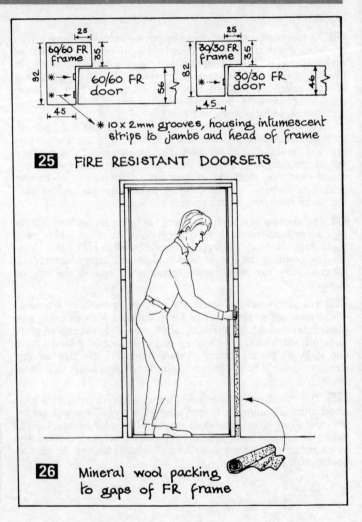

* 10 x 2mm grooves, housing intumescent strips to jambs and head of frame

25 FIRE RESISTANT DOORSETS

26 Mineral wool packing to gaps of FR frame

7 FIXING WINDOW FRAMES

An important consideration which determines the method of fixing window frames, is whether they are to be built-in as the brickwork proceeds, or fixed afterwards in the openings formed in the brickwork.

This decision is related to the type of windows being installed and whether they are robust enough to withstand the ordeal of being used as profiles at the 'green' brickwork stage.

Casement or pivot-type windows made of wood or galvanized steel, are usually built-in as the brickwork proceeds. The steel windows are supplied with fixing lugs that bolt on to the sides and project to be built-in to the bed joints. The wooden windows are fixed in a similar fashion, but with fixing devices obtained separately. These devices, traditionally referred to as *frame cramps*, are covered in detail in Chapter 6. Essentially, according to the type used, they are either screwed or hammered into the wooden side-jambs, as the brickwork rises, to be built-in to the bed joints. Two to three cramps each side is normal.

1 Like built-in door frames, these windows, after being positioned, are plumbed and supported at the head with one or two weighted scaffold boards pitched up from the oversite or floor. If the windows have a separate cill of stone or pre-cast concrete, usually these must be bedded first and protected with temporary boards on their outer face sides and edges. Projecting cills formed with sloping bricks-on-edge, are usually built at a later stage, the windows having been packed up accordingly to allow for this.

2 Aluminium windows, unless in a wooden sub frame, are usually fixed after the opening is formed, by screw fixings drilled and plugged into the masonry. To ensure the correct size of opening for this, temporary wooden profile frames of ex. 50 × 50 mm or 75 × 50 mm section, with 6 mm plywood corner plates, as illustrated, are constructed and placed in position during the brickwork operation.

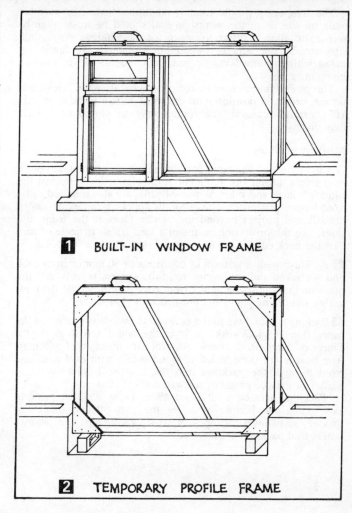

1 BUILT-IN WINDOW FRAME

2 TEMPORARY PROFILE FRAME

The temporary profile frames, mentioned overleaf, may be made on site or in the workshop and should be made slightly oversize to allow a fitting tolerance for the window. Any small gaps around the window, when fitted, should eventually be sealed with a gunned mastic bead run around the reveals of the opening.

The profile frames may be removed soon after the brickwork has set, or left in position until the windows are to be installed. After careful removal, the frames may be stored or reused immediately.

WINDOW BOARDS

Windows must be fixed into position before plastering takes place to enable a satisfactory abutment of the plaster-lining against the window's head and sides. Window boards are also required to be fixed before plastering. These boards appear as an extension of the cill and project beyond the plaster faces at the front and sides, like the projecting nosing of a stair tread. If made of timber, the back edge is usually tongued into a groove in the cill.

3 As illustrated, a portion of board about 50 mm in from each end is marked and cut on site, to fit the window reveals, and the machined nosing shape on the front edge is returned on the ends with a smoothing plane and finished with glasspaper.

4 Packing is usually required between the window board and the inner skin of blockwork, to level the board across its depth. Pieces of damp-proof course or hardboard make ideal packings. The boards are skew-nailed to wooden cills with oval nails and fixed through the packings into the blockwork with cut clasp nails – or may be plugged, screwed and pelleted.

Packings may be established about every 450 mm prior to positioning the board, by using the end offcuts, tongue-in-groove, spirit level on top – or try-square against the jambs – whilst trial packings are inserted.

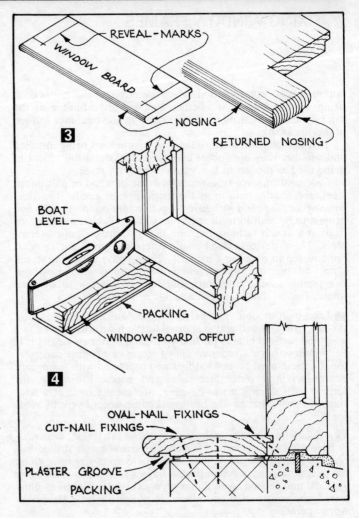

BOXFRAME WINDOWS

Traditional boxframe windows with double hanging/sliding sashes, sash cords, pulley wheels and cast-iron weights were quite common many years ago and are still very much in evidence in mature properties. For this reason, they may still be required in their traditional form, as replacement windows during maintenance operations.

It is unlikely that they would be used in this form in modern dwellings, because the presentday version of boxframe windows dispenses with the box construction, cords, pulley wheels and weights, and has solid jambs, heads and cills – and sliding sashes hung on spiral-balance fittings. Such windows, because of their smaller, solid jambs, would be fixed with frame cramps, etc. as already described for wooden casement or pivot windows.

REPLACING TRADITIONAL WINDOWS

5 Site measurements can be taken from the window being replaced and should be in agreement with the following considerations. The overall height and width of the frame should be at least 12 mm less than the brick opening to allow for fitting tolerances – and the outer linings of the box should only project 16 mm into the window opening, with the exception of the window's head in relation to a segmental brick-arch, where the 16 mm projection is taken at the extreme ends of the springing line.

6 When replacing the window, the wooden cill should be generously bedded on mastic, the frame levelled and plumbed and hardwood wedges should be driven in each side, top and bottom, immediately behind the ends of the pulley-stile head and the cill, against the brickwork – taking care not to push the frame out of square. Traditionally, skew-nail fixings were now driven through the inner-lining edges into plugs in the brickwork – although a better method would be to pre-fix short lengths of metal 'L'-shaped restraint straps to the sides of the box, to be fixed to the face of the brickwork when the box was wedged up in position. Finally, a sand-and-cement and/or mastic joint should be run around the head and reveals on the outside and the mastic joint on the cill should be repointed on the face edge. The window board or nosing should be nailed into the groove on the inside.

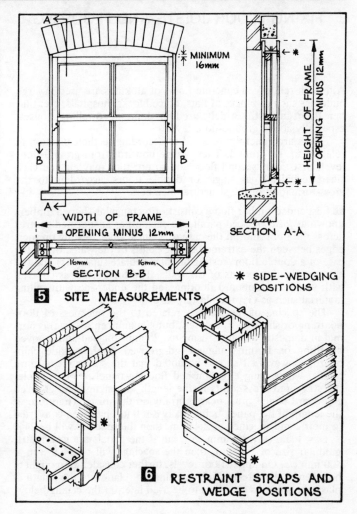

MINIMUM 16mm

HEIGHT OF FRAME = OPENING MINUS 12mm

SECTION A-A

WIDTH OF FRAME = OPENING MINUS 12mm

16mm   16mm

SECTION B-B

* SIDE-WEDGING POSITIONS

5 SITE MEASUREMENTS

6 RESTRAINT STRAPS AND WEDGE POSITIONS

8 FIXING FLOOR JOISTS AND FLOORING

Although reinforced concrete floors of all kinds are used in large buildings such as blocks of flats, office blocks, hospitals, etc. timber floors are still widely used in domestic dwelling houses, especially above ground-floor level.

Floors are generally referred to according to their position in relation to the ground. These range upwards from ground-floor level, first floor, second floor and so on; they may also be classified technically as single or double floors, according to the cross-formation of the structural members.

1 Suspended timber floors consist of rectangular-shaped timbers known as *joists*, spaced parallel to each other at specified centres across the floor and, in the case of a single floor, resting on their edges between the extreme bearing points of the walls, or, in the case of a double floor, resting on intermediate support(s) and the extreme bearing points of the walls. The top surface is covered with wood or chipboard flooring and the underside with ceiling material such as Gyproc plasterboard.

The spacing of the joists is related to the thickness of floor boarding or sheeting to be used, but 400 mm centres (c/c) is normal in domestic dwellings using ex. 25 mm tongued-and-grooved boarding or 18 mm tongued-and-grooved flooring-grade chipboard. However, it should be noted that the spacings are more critical when using edge-finished flooring panels. For example, the staggered cross-joints in the length of tongued-and-grooved chipboard panels must bear centrally on the joists. Therefore, if the length of the panel, being really 8 ft 0 in., has been converted to metric and specified as 2.440 m, then the spacings will be 2440 ÷ 6 = 406.6 (say 406 mm c/c), but if the panels are to a metric modular size of 2.400 m, then the spacings will be 2400 ÷ 6 = 400 mm c/c. On upper-floor levels, further consideration ought to be given to the effect of joist spacings in relation to the length of plasterboard laths or sheets to be used later on the ceiling below.

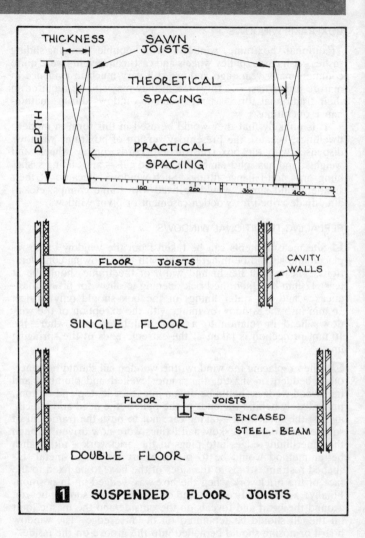

1 SUSPENDED FLOOR JOISTS

STRUCTURALLY-GRADED TIMBER

The sectional size of joists is always specified and need not concern the site carpenter or builder. The subject enters into the theory of structures and mechanics and is, therefore, a separate area of study. However, for domestic dwellings, a simple rule-of-thumb calculation has existed in the trade for many years, expressed as:

$$\frac{span}{2} + 2$$

but this is only an approximate method. In imperial measurement, this was expressed as:

Depth of joist in inches $= \dfrac{span\ in\ feet}{2} + 2$.

For example,

span of joists = 14 ft 0 in $\therefore$ Depth of joist $= \dfrac{14}{2} + 2 = 9$ in

In metric, the formula can be converted to:

Depth of joist in centimetres $= \dfrac{span\ in\ decimetres}{2} + 2$.

For example,

span of joists = 4.0 m $\therefore$ Depth of joist $= \dfrac{40}{2} + 2 = 22$ cm, i.e. 220 mm.

The thickness of joist, by this method, is usually standardized at 50 mm. The nearest commercial size, therefore, would be 225 × 50 mm.

By comparison, the table for floor joists given in Schedule 6 of the Building Regulations, specifies joists of 200 × 38 mm section, at 400 mm centres, for a maximum span of 4.0 m. However, it should be noted that structurally-graded timber is specified.

2 Such timber is now commonly specified for structural uses and is covered by BS 4978: 1973: *Timber grades for structural use.* Certain standards and criteria are laid down regarding the size of knots, slope of grain, etc. and the way in which the timber is to be examined and stamped accordingly in one of two grades.

3 Timber stamped with GS (*general structural*) and SS (*special structural*) has been visually graded by a BSI (British Standards Institute) authorized examiner – and timber stamped MGS (*machine general structural*) and MSS (*machine special structural*), refers to the same two grades which have been mechanically graded by a special grading machine, approved by the BSI authority or its agents.

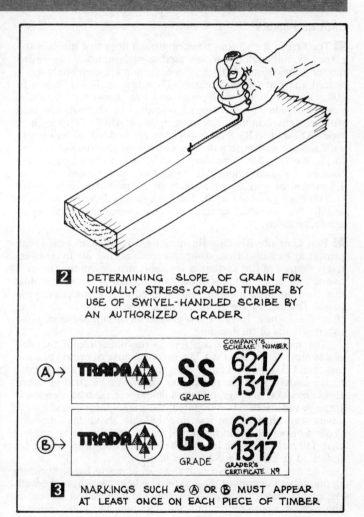

2 DETERMINING SLOPE OF GRAIN FOR VISUALLY STRESS-GRADED TIMBER BY USE OF SWIVEL-HANDLED SCRIBE BY AN AUTHORIZED GRADER

Ⓐ→ TRADA SS 621/1317

Ⓑ→ TRADA GS 621/1317

3 MARKINGS SUCH AS Ⓐ OR Ⓑ MUST APPEAR AT LEAST ONCE ON EACH PIECE OF TIMBER

GROUND FLOORS

4 The first of the various types of ground floor that involves the carpenter, although not widely used nowadays, is the suspended timber floor. Joists of 100 × 50 mm section are commonly used, spaced apart at 400 mm centres. They rest on 100 × 50 mm to 100 × 75 mm timber wall-plates and are skew-nailed to these from each side with 100 mm r.h.w. nails – or alternatively fixed with modern framing anchors such as 'MAFCO' Trip-L-Grip, type 'AL' and 'AR'. The wall plates are bedded on half-brick-wide sleeper walls with a damp-proof-course material sandwiched in the mortar joint. The sleeper walls, which should be honey-combed for under-floor air circulation, are spaced apart at 1.8 m centres – or to a maximum of 2.2 m if structural graded (GS) timber joists are used. The honeycombed sleeper walls are usually built onto the concrete oversite, rather than onto separate foundations.

5 Part C of the Building Regulations, which is concerned with protecting buildings from dampness, requires the site to be effectively cleared of turf and other vegetable matter and the concrete oversite to be of 100 mm minimum thickness and to a specified mix, laid on clean hardcore and finished with a trowel or spade finish. The top surface of the concrete oversite must be not lower than the highest level of the ground or paving adjoining the external walls of the building.

The space above the concrete to the underside of the wall plates must be not less than 75 mm (one course of bricks) and not less than 125 mm (one course of bricks + a 50 mm thick wall plate) to the underside of the joists. The space must be clear of debris (broken bricks, shavings, offcuts of timber, etc.) and be adequately through-ventilated. As illustrated, the damp-proof course in the cavity wall must be not less than 150 mm above the adjoining ground or paving – and the top of the cavity-fill must be not less than 150 mm below the level of the lowest damp-proof course (as indicated at **15**, *surface-battened floor*).

The first operation is to cut the wall plates to length, bearing in mind that the ends of these should be kept away from the walls by approximately 12 mm. After laying and spreading mortar on the sleeper walls, rolling out and flattening the DPC material, more mortar is laid and the wall plates are bedded and levelled into position with a spirit level.

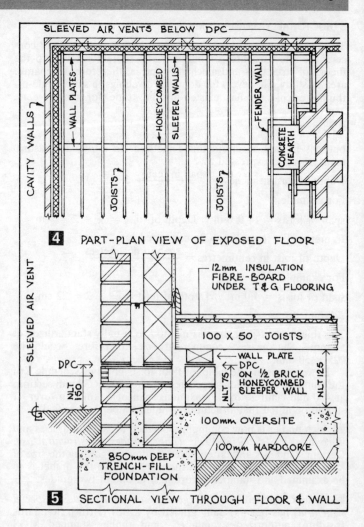

4 PART-PLAN VIEW OF EXPOSED FLOOR

5 SECTIONAL VIEW THROUGH FLOOR & WALL

6 Once the first wall plate has been bedded and levelled lengthwise, the others, as well as being levelled in length, must also be checked crosswise, using the first plate as a datum. If any wall plate cannot be laid in one piece, or changes direction, it should be jointed with a half-lap joint.

7 When the wall plates are set, the joists can be cut to length and fixed into position by nailing or anchoring – bearing in mind that the ends of the joists should also be kept away from the walls by approximately 12 mm. The first joist is fixed parallel to the wall, with a 50 mm gap running along its wall-side face to create more reliable edge-bearings and to facilitate easier board fixings. The second joist can be fixed at 400 mm centres from the first if timber boarding is to be used, but if edge-finished flooring panels are to be used, then the second joist should be fixed at 400 or 406 mm + expansion gap *from the wall* – not the first joist. Subsequent joists are fixed at the required spacing until the opposite wall is reached. The last spacing is usually under or slightly over size. Joists joined on sleeper walls are normally overlapped and side-nailed, as illustrated.

8 If a fireplace and a concrete hearth protrude into the floor area, the hearth is usually contained below floor level within a one-brick-thick *fender wall* built around the fireplace. The ends of the joists rest on wall plates supported by half the thickness of the fender wall. The other half supports the concrete hearth. Part L of the Building Regulations stipulates that no timber must come nearer to the fire opening than 500 mm from the front and 150 mm from each side, as at **8a** .

Although not legally required by the Regulations, ideally the timbers should be pre-treated or treated on site with a preservative.

The flooring material can be of minimum 18 mm flooring-grade chipboard or plywood, ex. 25 mm square-edged boarding or, more commonly, tongued-and-grooved boarding. To improve the thermal insulation of the floor, sheets of 12 mm bitumen-impregnated fibreboard should be laid across the joists, closely butted and sparingly nailed with 38 mm wire nails, immediately prior to floor-laying.

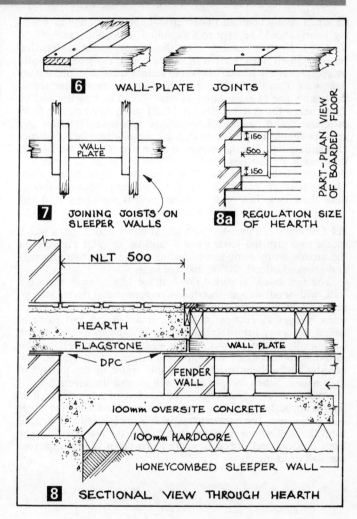

6 WALL-PLATE JOINTS

PART-PLAN VIEW OF BOARDED FLOOR

WALL PLATE

7 JOINING JOISTS ON SLEEPER WALLS

150
500
150

8a REGULATION SIZE OF HEARTH

NLT 500

HEARTH

WALL PLATE

FLAGSTONE

DPC

FENDER WALL

100mm OVERSITE CONCRETE

100mm HARDCORE

HONEYCOMBED SLEEPER WALL

8 SECTIONAL VIEW THROUGH HEARTH

9 When laying boarded floors, cross-joints (end grain or heading joints) should be kept to a minimum, if possible, and widely scattered. No two heading joints should line up on consecutive boards. On all sides, boards should be kept away from the walls by approximately 12 mm. This is to reduce the risk of picking up dampness from the walls and to allow for any movement across the boards due to expansion. All nails should be punched in 2 to 3 mm below the surface. Boards should be cramped up and fixed progressively in batches of five to six at a time. Tongues and grooves should be protected during cramping by placing offcuts of boarding between the cramps and the floor's edge. Nails – cut floor-brads or lost-head nails – should be about 2½ times the thickness of the board, i.e. 20 mm boards × 2½ = 50 mm nails. There should be two nails to each board fixing, about 16 mm in from the edges. Just prior to fixing, boards must be sorted and turned up the right way, as illustrated.

10 Cramping can be done with patent metal floor cramps which saddle and grip the joists when wound up to exert pressure on the boards, or by using sets of folding wedges cut from tongued-and-grooved offcuts, 200 to 300 mm long.

The first board is nailed down about 12 mm away from the wall, with small wedges inserted to retain the gap during cramping. Five or six more boards are cut to length and laid. When using wedges as cramps, a seventh board is cut and partially nailed, set away from the laid boards at a distance equal to the least width of the pre-cut folding wedges. The wedges are inserted at about 1 to 1.5 m centres and driven in to a tight fit. The boards, having been marked over the centre of the joists, are then nailed. When complete, the wedges and the seventh board are released. This board becomes the first of another batch of boards to be laid and the sequence is repeated until the other wall is reached. The final batch of boards are levered and wedged from the wall with a crowbar, then nailed; the last board having been checked and ripped to width to ensure a 12 mm gap from the wall on completion.

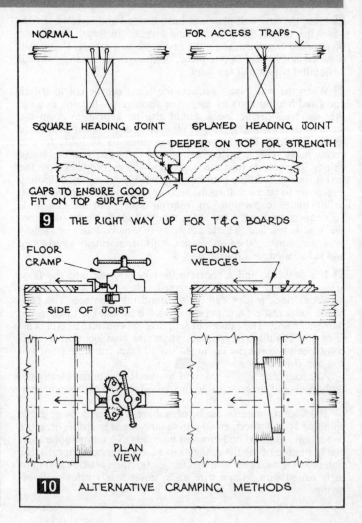

NORMAL

FOR ACCESS TRAPS

SQUARE HEADING JOINT   SPLAYED HEADING JOINT

DEEPER ON TOP FOR STRENGTH

GAPS TO ENSURE GOOD FIT ON TOP SURFACE

9 THE RIGHT WAY UP FOR T&G BOARDS

FLOOR CRAMP   FOLDING WEDGES

SIDE OF JOIST

PLAN VIEW

10 ALTERNATIVE CRAMPING METHODS

Floating floor (with continuous support)

11 This modern type of floor, consisting of jointed chipboard laid on an underlay of rigid polystyrene sheets or other material such as fibre insulating board, resin-bonded glass fibre slab, mineral wool slab, etc. and held down by its own weight and the perimeter skirting, turns a cold unyielding concrete base into a warm resilient floor at relatively low cost. Flooring-grade chipboard of minimum 18 mm thickness is used, which should be to BS 5669 : 1979, Type II (standard) or Type II/III (moisture resistant), tongued and grooved on all edges – such as Weyroc's Teegee 4.

The concrete oversite of 100 mm minimum thickness must be sealed with a damp-proof membrane (DPM), which may be sandwiched, at the bottom or on top of the concrete. If on top, in the form of an applied liquid DPM, this may replace the vapour check normally required, providing it is compatible with the polystyrene insulation boards to be laid upon it. One such liquid damp-proofing material which meets this requirement, is known as 'Liquapruf'.

Alternatively, an underlay of closely-butted sheets of expanded polystyrene, such as 19 mm or 25 mm Jablite flooring, is laid over the concrete surface (which should have been tamped to a level finish and allowed to dry thoroughly) and sheet-polythene of 1000-gauge minimum thickness is rolled out and laid over it to act as a vapour check. This should be turned up at least 38 mm at wall edges and all joints lapped 150 mm and sealed with waterproof adhesive tape, such as Sellotape 1408.

Next, the tongued-and-grooved chipboard panels are laid, taking care not to damage the polythene and leaving an expansion gap of 10 to 12 mm around all walls and other abutments. The cross-joints must be staggered to form a stretcher-bond pattern and all joints should be glued with polyvinyl acetate adhesive, such as Evo-Stik Resin W. Laying is started against the wall from one corner and when the other is reached, any reasonable-sized offcut can be returned to start the next row. Temporary wedges should be inserted around perimeter gaps until the glue hardens. A protective batten should be held against the flooring edge when hammering panels into position. Finally, before fixing the skirting, the perimeter gap should be checked and cleaned out, if necessary.

Other points concerning floating floors are as follows. All electric conduits, gas and water pipes should be accommodated within the oversite slab, or, alternatively, within the insulation

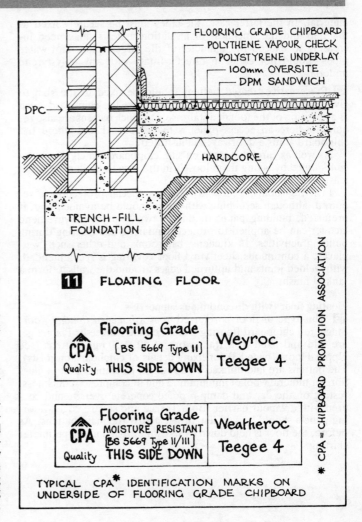

11 FLOATING FLOOR

TYPICAL CPA* IDENTIFICATION MARKS ON UNDERSIDE OF FLOORING GRADE CHIPBOARD

* CPA = CHIPBOARD PROMOTION ASSOCIATION

material. In the latter case, the pipes must be securely fixed to the slab and the thickness of insulation material may need increasing to exceed the diameter of the largest pipe. Hot-water pipes should not come in direct contact with any polystyrene underlay.

12 Preservative-treated battens should be fixed to the slab to give support to any concentrated load above the chipboard, such as a partition or the foot of a staircase, etc. Such battens are also required where an access panel is to be formed and where the chipboard abuts a doorway, as illustrated.

As well as careful storage on site, chipboard panels should be *conditioned* by laying them loosely in the area to be floored for at least 24 hours before fixing.

In living-rooms, bedrooms, etc. no special protection is required, although scrubbing with water should be avoided and, if preferred, building paper or one or two coats of polyurethene lacquer can be applied to protect standard-grade flooring during building activities. In kitchens, bathrooms and other such 'wet' places, a continuous sheet-vinyl floor covering is recommended, with welded joints and upturned edges around the walls to form a tanked finish.

Floating floor (with discontinuous support)
13 This type of floor is referred to as a *battened floating floor*. Staggered chipboard flooring panels, either Teegee or Plainedge, are laid and fixed to a framework of 50 × 50 mm battens (see Upper Floors (page 83) for fixing details of chipboard on joists). The battens are laid unfixed on a resilient insulating quilt of glass fibre or mineral wool of minimum 13 mm uncompressed thickness, resting on the dry and damp-proofed concrete oversite and covered with a vapour barrier. Both Teegee and square-edged flooring panels should be laid lengthwise *across* the main battens. As before, the floor is held down by its own weight and the perimeter skirting.

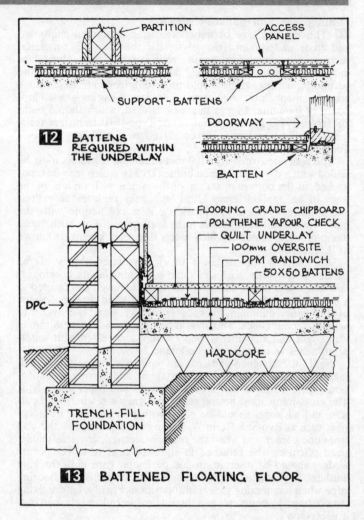

12 BATTENS REQUIRED WITHIN THE UNDERLAY

— PARTITION
— ACCESS PANEL
— SUPPORT-BATTENS
— DOORWAY →
— BATTEN

— FLOORING GRADE CHIPBOARD
— POLYTHENE VAPOUR CHECK
— QUILT UNDERLAY
— 100mm OVERSITE
— DPM SANDWICH
— 50×50 BATTENS

DPC →

HARDCORE

TRENCH-FILL FOUNDATION

13 BATTENED FLOATING FLOOR

Another type of floor to be considered, consists of 50 × 50 mm sawn fillets or battens, spaced at 400 mm centres (or 600 mm if 22 mm thick chipboard is used) and either embedded in the concrete oversite or fixed on top. Both of these applications are now controlled by Part C of the Building Regulations and the detailed examples given here are aimed at meeting the *C5 Deemed-to-satisfy provisions for floors of solid construction incorporating timber.*

Embedded-fillet floor

14 The timber fillets are splayed to a dovetail shape and must be pressure-treated with preservative in accordance with BS 4072 : 1974, prior to being inserted in the floor. The concrete oversite must incorporate a damp-proof sandwich membrane consisting of a continuous layer of hot applied soft bitumen of coal tar pitch not less than 3 mm thick, or at least three coats of bitumen solution, bitumen/rubber emulsion or tar/rubber emulsion. After the DPM has been applied and has set, the splayed fillets, having been cut to length and the cut-ends resealed with preservative, are bedded in position at 400 mm centres and levelled. This can be done by placing small deposits of concrete in which the fillets are laid and tamped to level positions. When set, the top half of the concrete sandwich is laid, using the fillets as screeding rules.

Surface-battened floor

15 A damp-proof sandwich membrane, as described above, is required and must be joined to the damp-proof course in the walls. Standard or Acoustic 'Bull Dog' floor clips can be used to hold the battens in position at the required spacing. The clips are pushed into the plastic concrete at 600 mm centres within 30 minutes of laying and levelling. A raised plank is placed across the concrete to support the operative and a batten marked with the clip-centres is used to act as a guide for spacing and aligning the clips. When laying the battened floor, after the concrete is set and thoroughly dry, the ears of the clips are raised with the claw hammer, the battens are inserted and fixed with special friction-tight nails supplied with the clips.

As illustrated, both floors may be insulated with 12-mm thick fibre insulation board and, if a chipboard floor is to be used, covered with a polythene vapour barrier.

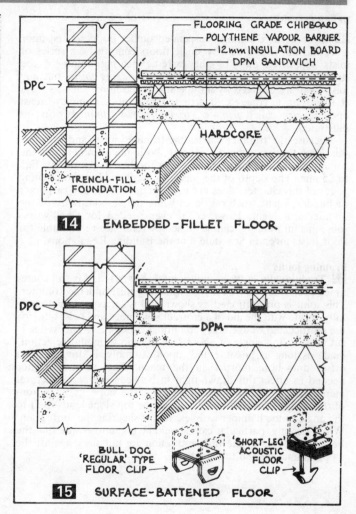

14 EMBEDDED-FILLET FLOOR

FLOORING GRADE CHIPBOARD
POLYTHENE VAPOUR BARRIER
12 mm INSULATION BOARD
DPM SANDWICH
DPC →
HARDCORE
TRENCH-FILL FOUNDATION

15 SURFACE-BATTENED FLOOR

DPC →
DPM
BULL DOG 'REGULAR' TYPE FLOOR CLIP →
'SHORT-LEG' ACOUSTIC FLOOR CLIP

UPPER FLOORS

16 In domestic dwellings, suspended timber floors at first-floor level and above are usually single floors comprising a series of joists supported only by the extreme bearing points of the structural walls. These joists are called *bridging joists*, but any joists that are affected by an opening in the floor, such as for a stairwell or a concrete hearth in front of a chimney-breast opening, are called *trimmer*, *trimming* and *trimmed joists*, as illustrated.

Because the trimmer carries the trimmed joists and transfers this load to the trimming joist(s), both the trimmer and the trimming joist are made thicker than the bridging joists by 12.5 to 25 mm. The depth of the joists, as mentioned in the opening pages of this chapter, does not usually concern the site carpenter or builder, such structural detail being the responsibility of the architectural team. However, if ever needed for small-works jobs, this information can be gained by reference to the table for floor joists given in Schedule 6 of the Building Regulations.

Framing joints

17 Traditionally, a tusk tenon joint was used – and is still sometimes preferred – between the trimming joist and the trimmer. This joint is proportioned as shown and is set out and cut carefully on site with the aid of a crosscut saw, brace and twist bits (for the mortice and wedge hole) and firmer chisels, etc. The wedge is cut to a shallow angle of about 1 in 10 ratio to inhibit rejection, made as long as possible and, upon assembly, is driven into a offset draw-bore mortice in the tenon. The offset clearance needed to effect this drawn-tight fit between the two structural members, is indicated in the illustration. The slope on the bottom of the wedge is to facilitate entry and the top slope lends itself to the angle of the hammer with less risk of shearing the short grain. When jointing, particular care should be taken to ensure that the bearing surfaces of the tusk and tenon are not slack against the stopped housing and the mortice.

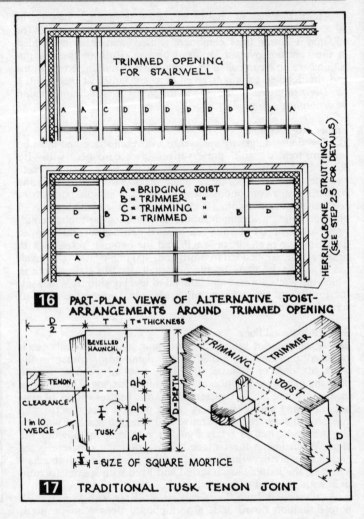

16 PART-PLAN VIEWS OF ALTERNATIVE JOIST-ARRANGEMENTS AROUND TRIMMED OPENING

A = BRIDGING JOIST
B = TRIMMER "
C = TRIMMING "
D = TRIMMED "

HERRINGBONE STRUTTING (SEE STEP 2.5 FOR DETAILS)

17 TRADITIONAL TUSK TENON JOINT

18 Traditional joints used between trimmed joists (D) and trimmer joist (B) vary between a *blind tenon* and a *plain stopped-housing*. Other joints, seen more in textbooks than in practice, include a *bevelled stopped-housing* and a *dovetailed stopped-housing*. The blind tenon joint is made to the same proportions as the common tusk tenon, but does not have a wedge or projecting tenon. The plain stopped-housing joint is set out and gauged to cut into the trimmer by 12.5 mm on the top edge and half the joist-depth on the side. It is formed by making three diagonal saw cuts across the grain, chopping a relief slot at the bottom of the housing and chisel-paring from above.

19 Metal timber-connectors are now being extensively used to replace the above-mentioned joints, in the form of metal framing anchors and timber-to-timber joist hangers. The advantages to be gained in using these connectors, are a saving of labour hours and, in the case of the hangers, more effective support of the trimmer or trimmed joists, by the bearing being at the bottom of the load.

When using sherardized framing anchors, such as 'MAFCO' Trip-L-Grip, for floor joists, the loads to be carried are such that each trimmed joist should comprise both a 'B'-type and a 'C'- or two 'C'-type anchors. When using two 'C'-types (CL and CR), on each side of the joist, they should be slightly staggered to avoid nail-lines clashing. The anchors are recommended to be fixed with 3 mm diameter × 30 mm-long sherardized clout nails.

20 Steel joist hangers, such as manufactured by Catnic-Holstran, type TT (timber to timber) S and L (short and long) are made from 1 mm galvanized steel with pre-punched nail holes. As illustrated, the straps are easily bent over the joists and fixed with 32 mm galvanized plasterboard nails. Another advantage of the thin-gauge metal is that hangers do not require housing into the top or bottom edges of joists.

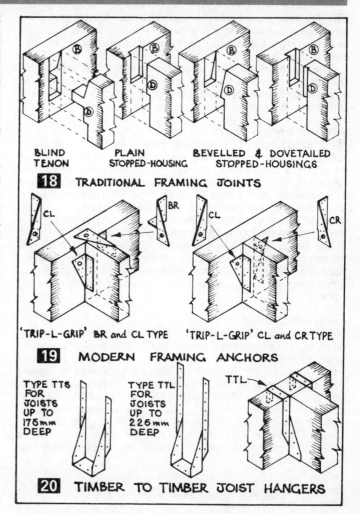

BLIND TENON   PLAIN STOPPED-HOUSING   BEVELLED & DOVETAILED STOPPED-HOUSINGS

18 TRADITIONAL FRAMING JOINTS

'TRIP-L-GRIP' BR and CL TYPE   'TRIP-L-GRIP' CL and CR TYPE

19 MODERN FRAMING ANCHORS

TYPE TTS FOR JOISTS UP TO 175mm DEEP

TYPE TTL FOR JOISTS UP TO 225mm DEEP

TTL

20 TIMBER TO TIMBER JOIST HANGERS

21   The joists should always bridge across the shortest span of an area, unless a double floor is required, whereby a steel beam (or beams) bridges the shortest span and the timber joists run the longest span, bearing on the beam(s), as illustrated.

The spacing of the joists, as mentioned on the first page of this chapter, is related to the thickness of flooring and the size of manufactured flooring panels and ceiling boards to be used: 400 mm to 406 mm joist-centres is usual.

Solid-wall bearings

22   The old practice of building the ends of joists into solid (non-cavity) walls is now frowned upon, because of the increased possibility of timber decay through lateral damp-penetration. As illustrated, the modern practice is to use steel joist hangers, such as manufactured by Catnic-Holstran, type TW (timber to wall), made from 2.5 mm galvanized steel. These hangers can also be used for timber to timber connections – and for this reason they have holes on the top flange as well as on the diagonal side straps. When fixing, 32-mm long galvanized plasterboard nails are recommended. Owing to a double metal-flange on the bottom, equalling a thickness of 5 mm, the bottom edge of the joists require notching out to retain a flat surface for the plasterboard ceiling.

Cavity-wall bearings

23   TW-, or, as illustrated. TWR-type joist hangers with a turn-down top flange to ensure correct and safe anchoring, especially when there is insufficient weight above, may be used for cavity walls. Alternatively, the ends of joists, which should be treated with timber preservative, are positioned, levelled up and built into the inner skin of the cavity wall. Care should be taken to ensure that the joists do not protrude past the inner face of the wall, into the cavity. The temporary positioning-batten, illustrated, should be attached to the scaffold or return wall at its end(s) to create stability and to stop the joists toppling sideways until they are built in.

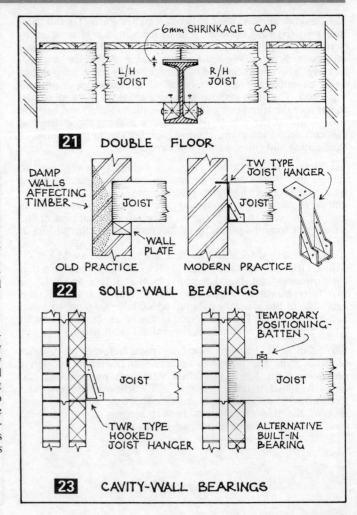

6mm SHRINKAGE GAP
L/H JOIST   R/H JOIST

21 DOUBLE FLOOR

DAMP WALLS AFFECTING TIMBER
JOIST
WALL PLATE
OLD PRACTICE

TW TYPE JOIST HANGER
JOIST
MODERN PRACTICE

22 SOLID-WALL BEARINGS

JOIST
TWR TYPE HOOKED JOIST HANGER

TEMPORARY POSITIONING-BATTEN
JOIST
ALTERNATIVE BUILT-IN BEARING

23 CAVITY-WALL BEARINGS

Strutting

Strutting in suspended timber floors is used to give additional strength by interconnection between joists. This is to effect equal distribution of the weight and to prevent joists bending sideways. Struts should be used where spans exceed 50 times the joist thickness. Therefore, with 50 mm thick joists, a single row of central struts should be used when the span exceeds 2.5 m and two rows are required for spans over 5 m and up to 7.5 m.

Solid strutting

24 The old practice of strutting the floor with solid noggings is now frowned upon as being costly in material, adding unnecessary weight and creating an inflexible floor.

Herringbone strutting

25 The traditional method, using 50 × 25 mm or 50 × 38 mm sawn timber, although still effective, nowadays has to compete with struts made of steel. With timber, the method of fixing involves marking a chalk line across the joists – usually in the centre of the floor – squaring the marks down the sides of the joists, then striking another line on top, parallel to the first and set apart by the joist-depth minus 20 to 25 mm. As illustrated, the strutting material is laid diagonally within these lines and marked from below to produce the required plumb-cuts (vertical faces of an angle). Cutting and fixing the struts is done in a kneeling position from above, using 50 to 63 mm r.h.w. nails. Prior to strutting, the joists running along each opposite wall should be packed – or wedged – and nailed immediately behind the line of struts.

Steel strutting

26 As illustrated, two types of galvanized steel herringbone struts are produced to compete with the above. The first type have upturned and down-turned lugs for fixings with minimum 38 mm long r.h.w. nails. As before, fixing is from above.

27 The second type, with the well-known 'BAT' trademark, has forked ends which simply bed themselves into the joists when forced in at the bottom and pulled down firmly at the top. This time, fixing is from below.

One disadvantage with steel strutting, which is made to suit joist centres of 400, 450 and 600 mm, is that there are always one or two places in any floor that do not conform to size and require reduced struts.

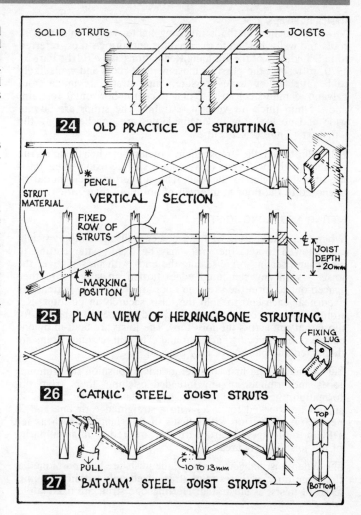

24 OLD PRACTICE OF STRUTTING

SOLID STRUTS — JOISTS

STRUT MATERIAL · PENCIL · VERTICAL SECTION · FIXED ROW OF STRUTS · MARKING POSITION · JOIST DEPTH – 20 mm

25 PLAN VIEW OF HERRINGBONE STRUTTING

FIXING LUG

26 'CATNIC' STEEL JOIST STRUTS

PULL · 10 TO 13 mm · TOP · BOTTOM

27 'BATJAM' STEEL JOIST STRUTS

Restraint straps

New construction methods involving lighter-weight materials in roofs and walls, has led to the need for anchoring straps, referred to in Schedule 7 of the Building Regulations and CP III : Part 2 : 1970, to restrict the possible movement of roofs and walls likely to be affected by wind pressure. Such straps are made from galvanized mild-steel strip, 5 mm thick for horizontal restraint and 2.5 mm thick for vertical restraint. The straps are 30 mm wide and up to 1.2 m in length. Holes are punched along the length at 15 mm offset centres.

28 As illustrated, the straps require notching-in when the joists run parallel to the wall, but only require surface-fixing when joists are at right angles to the wall. The supported walls should be anchored to the floor at intervals of not more than 2 m.

FITTING AND FIXING JOISTS

When the load-bearing walls have been built up to storey height and allowed to set, the joists may be fixed. After cutting to length and sealing or re-sealing the ends with preservative, the joists – with any cambered edges turned upwards – are then spaced out to form the skeleton floor and temporary battens are fixed near each end to hold the joists securely in position. Restraint straps at low level are fixed and notches may be cut for those that run across the joist tops. The joists are built-in by one course of blocks being laid all round. The top restraint straps are then fixed and blockwork may proceed.

29 Normally, the first consideration is to position the trimming joists and trimmer of any intended opening, then, from this formation, the trimmed and bridging joists are spaced out. Joists should be checked for level with a straightedge or line and, if necessary, packed up with offcuts of thin material such as felt DPC or oil-tempered hardboard – or lowered by minimal paring of the joist-bearing area.

30 When joist hangers are used, the joists are best positioned at the same time, with restraint straps fixed only within the upper areas of joists, as illustrated. Herringbone struts are fixed later.

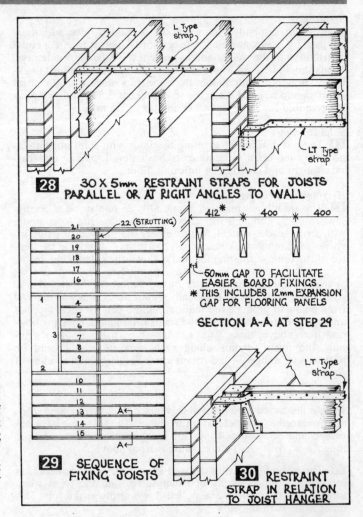

28 30 X 5mm RESTRAINT STRAPS FOR JOISTS PARALLEL OR AT RIGHT ANGLES TO WALL

412* — 400 — 400

50mm GAP TO FACILITATE EASIER BOARD FIXINGS.
* THIS INCLUDES 12mm EXPANSION GAP FOR FLOORING PANELS

SECTION A-A AT STEP 29

29 SEQUENCE OF FIXING JOISTS

30 RESTRAINT STRAP IN RELATION TO JOIST HANGER

CHIPBOARD FLOORING ON JOISTS

Flooring-grade chipboard of minimum 18 mm thickness, Type II (standard) or Type II/III (moisture resistant), either square edged (Plainedge), tongued and grooved on four edges (Teegee 4), or tongued and grooved on two long edges (Teegee 2), may be laid on suspended timber floors, whether at ground level or upper-floor level.

FIXING TEEGEE FLOORING

31 Teegee 2 or Teegee 4 boards, as illustrated, are laid with the long edges across the joists. The short edges bear centrally on the joists and *only* the long edges against the wall must be supported by noggings of at least 38 mm width – but preferably of 50 mm width and 75 mm depth. The boards should be nailed with four nails to each joist, two about 25 mm from each edge and two nails equidistant between. The nails should be 56 mm × 10 gauge annular-ring shank type. All joints should be glued with polyvinyl acetate adhesive.

FIXING PLAINEDGE FLOORING

32 Contrary to the Teegee flooring method, these boards are laid with the long edges bearing centrally on the joists. *All* short edges, including the edges against the walls must be supported with – preferably – 75 × 50 mm noggings as above, fixed securely between the joists. The boards should be fixed with 50 mm or 56 mm × 10 gauge annular-ring shank nails at 200 to 300 mm apart around the edges and at 400 to 500 mm apart on intermediate joists. Nails should be at least 9 mm in from the edges of boards and punched-in 2 to 3 mm below the surface.

Cross-joints on both types of board must be staggered and expansion gaps of 10 to 12 mm allowed around the perimeter of any abutment. Traps in the floor must be supported on all four edges and fixed with 50 mm × 8 gauge countersunk screws. As stated on floating floors, the chipboard panels should be *conditioned* before being fixed and protected according to its location.

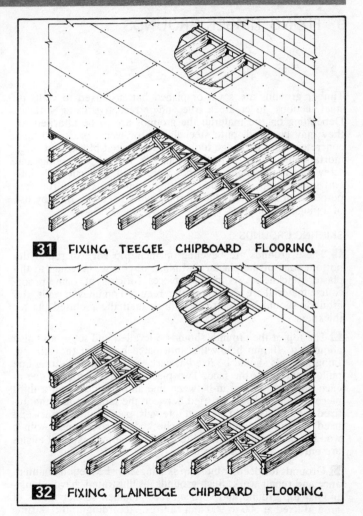

31 FIXING TEEGEE CHIPBOARD FLOORING

32 FIXING PLAINEDGE CHIPBOARD FLOORING

9 FIXING TIMBER GROUNDS

Timber grounds are sawn or planed battens, fixed to walls or steel sections, to create a true and/or receptive fixing surface. Depending on the material the grounds are to be attached to, they may be 'fired' onto steel flanges or webs, brickwork and concrete with a cartridge tool, fixed to aerated blocks and brick mortar-joints with cut, clasp nails, or fixed by plugging and screwing. Traditionally, grounds were fixed with cut nails into end grain, propeller-shaped plugs, driven into the mortar-free perpends of brickwork; the mortar having been cut away by use of a plugging chisel.

SKIRTING GROUNDS

1 These grounds are bevelled on their top edge to retain the bottom edge of the plaster and must, of course, be equal to the plaster thickness. As packing-pieces (offcuts of damp-proof-course material are ideal) are often required on uneven walls, the grounds should be slightly less thick than the required plaster thickness.

2 The top of the grounds should be levelled and set up to finish about 6 to 10 mm below the anticipated height of the skirting. Long grounds should be fixed at each end and have a string line pulled taut along the face. Two pieces of offcut ground, one at each end, are pushed in-between line and ground – and a third piece of offcut ground is tried between the taut line and the un-fixed ground at 600 to 900 mm intervals, packed if necessary and fixed. Shorter grounds may be checked for straightness with a wooden or aluminium straightedge. Internal and external angles are butt jointed – not mitred.

3 Grounds for deep or built-up skirtings may be met on maintenance and repair work. Such grounds, as illustrated, have a longitudinal top ground and vertical, face-plumbed soldier pieces of ground fixed at 600 to 900 mm centres. According to the skirting design and height, additional stepped soldiers may be fixed onto the first row.

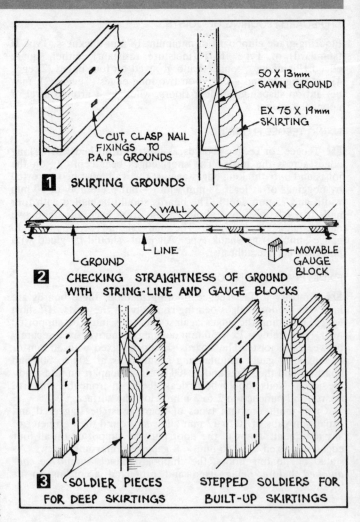

1 SKIRTING GROUNDS

CUT, CLASP NAIL FIXINGS TO P.A.R GROUNDS

50 X 13mm SAWN GROUND

EX 75 X 19mm SKIRTING

WALL — LINE — GROUND — MOVABLE GAUGE BLOCK

2 CHECKING STRAIGHTNESS OF GROUND WITH STRING-LINE AND GAUGE BLOCKS

3 SOLDIER PIECES FOR DEEP SKIRTINGS

STEPPED SOLDIERS FOR BUILT-UP SKIRTINGS

ARCHITRAVE GROUNDS

4 Because the modern architrave section is relatively narrow, the traditional use of grounds in these situations is rarely met with nowadays. Similar to skirting grounds, the edge against the plaster was bevelled and had to be concealed under the outer architrave edge by about 6 to 10 mm. These grounds helped to keep the wet plaster away from the lining's edges and provided a true, receptive fixing surface for the outer architrave edges.

APRON-LINING GROUNDS

5 Grounds are often used behind the apron lining around the edge of a trimmed stairwell. This is to bring the face of the lining to a position equal to the centre of the newel post and to further support the projecting landing-nosing. The grounds may be longitudinal and/or in the form of vertical soldier pieces. The latter gives better support by being across the grain to offset any cupping of the lining.

WALL-PANELLING GROUNDS

6 Grounds – without bevelled edges – may be fixed horizontally across a wall and spaced at 600 mm centres from floor to ceiling, as a true fixing medium for vertical boarding; or fixed vertically at similar centres across the wall as a true fixing medium for horizontal boarding. The technique in these situations is, having fixed one ground straight and true, it is used as a datum for all the other grounds to relate to, by straightedge or line.

FRAMED GROUNDS

7 Occasionally, on traditional forms of wall panelling, framed grounds are still used. Basically, these consist of grooved or morticed vertical grounds and tongued horizontal grounds that fit in-between the vertical members.

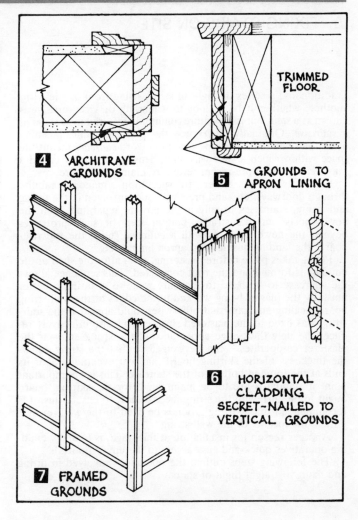

4 ARCHITRAVE GROUNDS

TRIMMED FLOOR

5 GROUNDS TO APRON LINING

6 HORIZONTAL CLADDING SECRET-NAILED TO VERTICAL GROUNDS

7 FRAMED GROUNDS

10 FIXING STAIRS ON SITE

Traditionally, a series or flight of steps, rising from one level to another, whether it be a floor to a landing or vice versa, was known as a *stair*, but is now more commonly referred to as *stairs* or a *staircase*. Originally, *stairs* was the plural of stair, meaning more than one flight of steps – and the word *staircase* meant the space within which a stair was built. This space is now called a *stair well*. These more-recent terms are mainly used here.

For reasons of easier transportation, manoeuvreability through doorways, etc. and practical issues involved in the fitting and fixing, staircases usually arrive on site separated from the newel posts and balustrade, bottom step (if such protrudes beyond the newel post, as with a bullnose step), the top riser board, the landing nosings and apron linings, etc.

Fixing takes place before plastering, soon after the shell of the building is formed and the roof completed. This sequence allows the staircase to be fixed to the bare wall, so ensuring a better finish by the plaster being worked to the edges of the wall-string board, sealing any gaps that otherwise would appear if the stair-string was fixed to the plastered surface. This also effectively reduces the ugly thick-edge appearance of the string and – if the plasterer co-operates – can be gauged so that the string equals the thickness of the skirting board that will eventually abut its ends at the top and bottom of the staircase. This is an important point if standards are to be maintained, for the skirting board ought to be flush with the string-face. In fact, to ensure this, it is recommended that skirting grounds be fixed to the wall, even if only in the locality of the wall string.

Another reason for installation at this stage, is to allow building operatives quick and easy access to the upper floor(s).

The following steps outline the operations involved in fitting and fixing a straight flight of stairs.

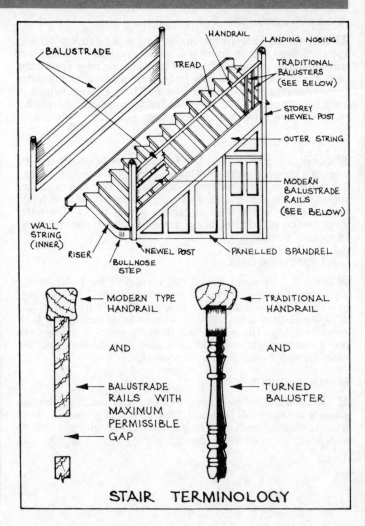

STAIR TERMINOLOGY

1 Check whether the existing floors (upper and lower) are finished levels. In the case of a boarded or ply/chipboard sheeted floor, these are usually the levels to work to – as any additional floor covering can be assumed to cover the steps as well, thereby retaining equal rises to all steps. If, however, the ground floor is of concrete and has yet to receive a finishing material such as a 50 mm sand/cement screed, or a floating floor of expanded polystyrene and tongued and grooved chipboard, or sand/cement screed and parquet blocks, etc. then the finished floor level (f.f.l.) must be known and established – and packing blocks or wedges prepared to fit under the bottom step.

2 At this stage of the job, the f.f.l. has usually been established and may be found ready to transfer from the bottom of door linings or external-door cills. Alternatively, a bench mark above the site datum can be levelled across to the stair area, marked on the wall and measured down the set amount to the f.f.l.

3 Next, cut the wall string at the bottom to fit the f.f.l. (even if the finished floor is yet to be laid). If not already cut or marked during manufacture, then simply measure down the depth-of-rise from the top of the first tread-housing (if such exists, as in the case of a bottom step left out for site-fixing) or measure down from the tread and mark a line through this point at right angles to the face of the first riser-housing or riser. Cut carefully on the waste side with a sharp crosscut or panel saw. Then mark the plumb cut to form the joint between the string and skirting board, as indicated. To do this, set the skirting height, say 95 mm, onto the blade of the combination mitre-square and square-up from the f.f.l. cut, sliding along until the corner of the blade touches the edge of the string. At this point, mark the plumb line and cut with a panel saw.

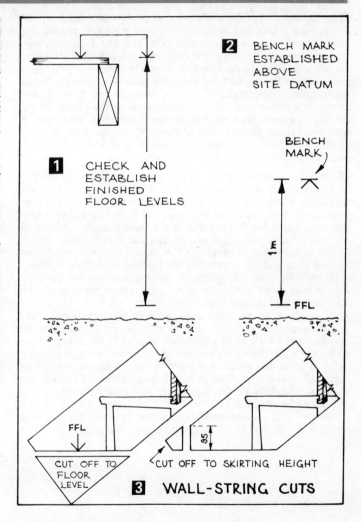

1 CHECK AND ESTABLISH FINISHED FLOOR LEVELS

2 BENCH MARK ESTABLISHED ABOVE SITE DATUM

BENCH MARK

FFL

FFL

CUT OFF TO FLOOR LEVEL

35

CUT OFF TO SKIRTING HEIGHT

3 WALL-STRING CUTS

4 At the top end of the wall string, more elaborate marking out and cutting is required to enable the staircase to fit against the landing/floor trimmer or trimming joist. This also includes preparation of the string to meet the skirting. As indicated, the cuts are made in four places. The first, within the riser housing, on a line equal to the back of the riser; the second, within the tread housing, on a line equal to the underside of the flooring; the third, on a plumb line equal approximately to the centre of the landing trimmer (this is for the skirting abutment); and fourth, a horizontal cut at the very top of the string, equal to the skirting height. This last cut should be planed to a smooth finish, as it becomes a visual edge of the string margin.

5 Offer the staircase up into position, resting against the landing and packed up at the bottom, if necessary. Check the treads across the width and depth with a spirit level. Any inaccuracies registering in the depth of the tread will infer that either a fundamental error has been made in the mathematical division of the total rise of the staircase, or that the floor-to-floor storey height is not what it should be. A more positive way of confirming this, will be to position the bottom newel post temporarily onto the outer-string tenons, making sure that the shoulder of the bare-faced tenon fits tightly, and check for plumb with the spirit level, as illustrated.

If inaccuracies are confirmed and they are only minor, they might have to be suffered, as very little can be done – short of shoddy tactics such as adjusting the shoulder of the string-tenons to improve the plumb appearance of the newel posts. If inaccuracies in level and plumb are more serious, measure the rise of one step carefully, multiply it by the total number of steps in the staircase and compare this figure with the actual measurement of the storey height from f.f.l. below to f.f.l. above.

Armed with this information, it would be wise to confer with the site foreman or builder's agent before proceeding.

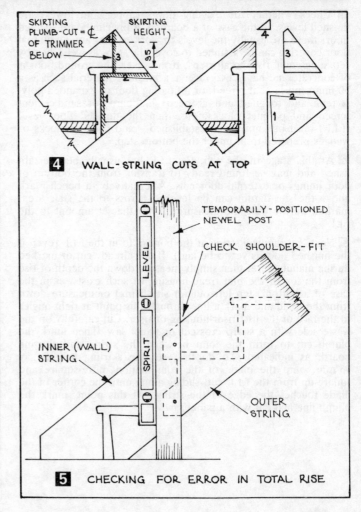

4 WALL-STRING CUTS AT TOP

SKIRTING PLUMB-CUT = ℄ OF TRIMMER BELOW

SKIRTING HEIGHT

95

TEMPORARILY-POSITIONED NEWEL POST

CHECK SHOULDER-FIT

LEVEL

SPIRIT

INNER (WALL) STRING

OUTER STRING

5 CHECKING FOR ERROR IN TOTAL RISE

6 After minor adjustments, if any, to the normal, correctly-fitting staircase, the next operation to consider is the fixing of the inner string to the wall. If the wall, being the inner skin of cavity construction, is built of insulation material such as Celcon or Thermalite blocks, then nailing with 100 mm cut, clasp nails will be satisfactory. These fixings are driven through the string on the underside of the treads, within the triangular area of every third or fourth step. However, if the wall, being of brick or concrete blocks, etc. is not receptive to direct nailing, then the wall string will have to be drilled to enable the wall to be marked for plugs and screw fixings. Alternatively, the string and the wall can be drilled through in one operation to receive recently-devised fixings consisting of countersunk screws fully encased in extended plastic plugs. These plugs would be inserted through the drilled face of the in-situ wood and screwed as normal. The extended plastic plug (which has a flared top edge to follow the counter-sinking) takes up the slackness in the normally-oversize shank hole.

7 Having decided on the method of fixing the wall string and, if necessary, having plugged the walls for same, the next job is to prepare the bottom newel post to meet the floor level. The post is usually left longer at its lower end to allow for site treatment in various ways, according to the construction of the floor. Unless specified, the carpenter himself decides exactly which way is suitable for a particular floor. The various methods of treatment at floor level are as follows.

(a) On concrete oversites, the newel post can be cut to rest on the concrete – although the end should be sealed with preservative and/or capped with a piece of damp-proof-course material. When, after installation of the staircase, the sand and cement floor screed, etc. is bedded and set around the post, a further degree of rigidity is achieved.

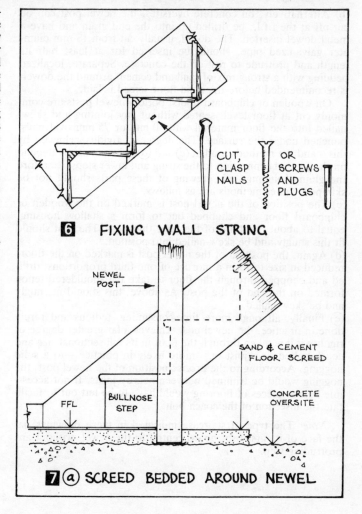

6 FIXING WALL STRING

CUT, CLASP NAILS

OR SCREWS AND PLUGS

NEWEL POST

SAND & CEMENT FLOOR SCREED

CONCRETE OVERSITE

FFL

BULLNOSE STEP

7 (a) SCREED BEDDED AROUND NEWEL

ⓑ Alternatively, on concrete oversites, the newel post can be cut off at the f.f.l., be drilled up into the end grain and have a metal dowel inserted. The dowel, usually cut from 18-mm diameter galvanized pipe, should be inserted for at least half its length and protrude to rest on the concrete. Separate, localized bedding with a strong mix of sand and cement around the dowel, is recommended before the main floor screed is laid.

On wooden or chipboard floors, bottom newel posts are commonly cut at floor level, seated without any jointing and skew-nailed into the floor material with 50 mm or 75 mm oval nails, punched under the surface. The degree of rigidity achieved by this – and the methods used at ⓒ and ⓓ below – mainly depend on the jointed connection to the string and lower steps: therefore the gluing, pinning and screwing of these parts should not be skimped. Other methods are as follows.

ⓒ The position of the newel post is marked on the wooden or chipboard floor and chopped out to form a shallow housing, equal to about one-third of the floor thickness. The post should fit this snugly and be skew-nailed into position.

ⓓ Again, the position of the newel post is marked on the floor, reduced in size to form a mortice of one-third proportions, drilled and chopped through the floor to take the shouldered tenon formed on the end of the post. As above, this should fit snugly and be skew-nailed.

ⓔ Finally, although more time-consuming, tedious and rarely done in practice, the newel post achieves a far greater degree of rigidity if it is taken through the floor in its full sectional size and coach-bolted to a joist or – more likely in practice – to a solid nogging. According to the precise position of the newel post, the nogging would be trimmed between nearby joists. If not accessible below, pieces of flooring would have to be left out to facilitate the insertion of the coach bolt.

Note: The type of staircase indicated in these drawings has the face of its first riser board central to the newel, without any protruding step.

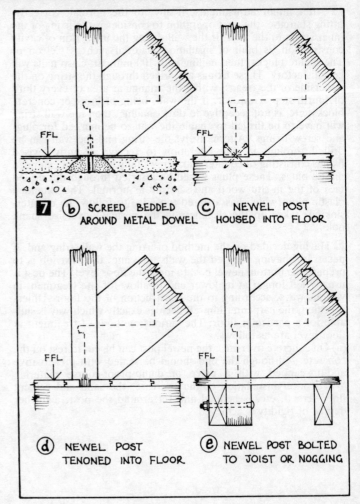

7 ⓑ SCREED BEDDED AROUND METAL DOWEL   ⓒ NEWEL POST HOUSED INTO FLOOR

ⓓ NEWEL POST TENONED INTO FLOOR   ⓔ NEWEL POST BOLTED TO JOIST OR NOGGING

The bottom newel post, which will have been morticed and fitted during manufacture, is now ready to be permanently fixed to the outer string. This can be done with the staircase laying on its side or, if not possible, resting up against the landing above and seated on saw stools, etc. at the bottom. The mortice and tenon joint should already be drilled to receive 12 mm diameter wooden dowels (pins). The holes will be slightly offset to enable the tapered pins to effect a wedging action when driven in, so drawing up the shoulders of the oblique (uncrampable) tenons to a good fit against the post.

8 If pins are not supplied, cut off pieces of 12 mm diameter dowel rod, about 50 mm longer than the newel thickness and chisel the ends to a slow taper of about 25 mm length. After trying the newel post into position, coat the joint with polyvinyl acetate glue and reposition the newel. This is best done by using a claw hammer onto a spare block of wood held against the lower face of the newel. When a reasonable fit has been achieved, a touch of glue is placed into the draw-bore holes and the tapered pins are driven in until no part of the taper remains within the newel – bearing in mind, though, that the lower dowel usually clashes with the step on the other side. Clean off excess glue with a damp rag or paper and then cut off the surplus dowel ends with a tenon or bead saw, near the newel's surface. Clean off remainder with a block plane or smoothing plane.

9 Assuming that the staircase has a bullnose or splay-ended bottom step, which protrudes beyond the newel post, this is the next to be fixed. It should be realized that such steps cannot be attached during manufacture, without the newel being permanently in position. The step may have to be fitted and, as illustrated, this usually involves slight easings to the front end of the tread entering the string housing and the rear end of the tread and face of bullnosed riser entering the newel post housings. After a successful dry fit, glue the step into position and drive in the glued string wedges; screw the bottom edge of the second riser to the tread and, finally, screw the ends of the bottom two risers into the housings of the newel post.

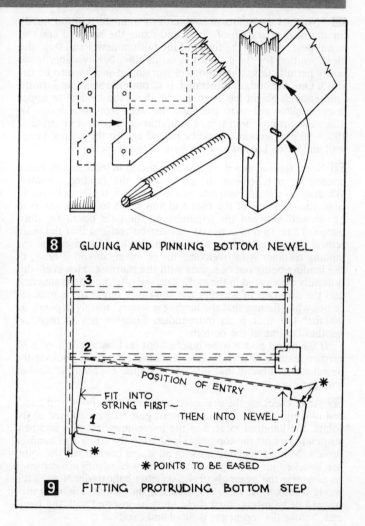

8 GLUING AND PINNING BOTTOM NEWEL

9 FITTING PROTRUDING BOTTOM STEP

POSITION OF ENTRY

FIT INTO STRING FIRST ~ THEN INTO NEWEL

* POINTS TO BE EASED

10 Now set the staircase back into its ultimate position, ready for the next operation of fitting and fixing the handrail and top newel post. As with the fixing of the bottom newel and step, the ideal position for the staircase is on its side, but available space rarely permits this, so methods of working in-situ have to be devised. One method, as illustrated, is to push the staircase forward until enough height has been gained above the landing or upper floor to allow access to complete the work from that level. To make this arrangement safe, a temporary kicker strut or struts of 100 × 50 mm section, should be lodged against the nearest cross-wall and extend to support the base of the staircase.

11 Next, the top newel may need reducing in thickness by being housed or notched-out in the area of the landing trimmer. Whether this is necessary or not depends on the newel's thickness, the thickness of the riser and how much tolerance gap is to be allowed between the trimmer and the riser board (as illustrated, 12 to 18 mm is usual). It must be realized that the main reason for any allowance between the back of the riser and the landing trimmer is to overcome the problem, should it arise, of the landing being out of square with the staircase. However, this is usually discovered in the early stages of offering up the staircase and the question of whether the allowance ought to be retained or not when finding that the landing is square, mainly depends on whether the stair is an independent flight or has to relate to another landing at the bottom.

If the newel post is to be notched-out, as illustrated, it must be further realized that this has a certain advantage of hooking the newel – and thereby that side of the staircase – onto the landing trimmer.

12 After checking the dry assembly of the newel post and handrail in conjunction with both newels, glue may be applied to the joints, the handrail located in the lower-newel mortice and held suspended whilst the top newel is fitted to the string and handrail tenons. Moving speedily, as with all gluing operations, the joints are knocked up and the glue-coated draw-bore pins are driven-in to complete the assembly of the skeleton balustrade. Note that if modern balustrade rails, morticed into the newels, are being used instead of balusters, then these must be inserted with the handrail, before the top newel is fitted and fixed.

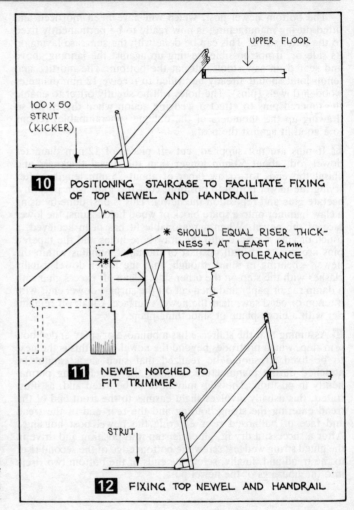

UPPER FLOOR

100 × 50 STRUT (KICKER)

10 POSITIONING STAIRCASE TO FACILITATE FIXING OF TOP NEWEL AND HANDRAIL

✳ SHOULD EQUAL RISER THICKNESS + AT LEAST 12mm TOLERANCE

11 NEWEL NOTCHED TO FIT TRIMMER

STRUT

12 FIXING TOP NEWEL AND HANDRAIL

13 Before the staircase can be set back into position, the top riser and landing-nosing have to be fitted and fixed to each other, to the string housings, the newel post housings and to the adjacent tread. This operation is often skimped, resulting in a loose top riser and a squeaky top step. To avoid this, attend to all the following points.

Check that the rebated side of the nosing is equal to the flooring thickness and, if thicker, ease with a rebate plane. Then measure between the housings and cut the nosing and riser to the correct length. Now, because this particular step cannot have glue blocks set into its inner angle like the other steps (as they would clash with the trimmer), the best way to strengthen the joint is by *pocket screwing*. This is achieved by gouging or drilling shallow niches into the upper back-side of the riser board and by drilling oblique shank holes through these to create at least three fixings to the nosing piece. The riser is also drilled to receive two screws at each end and three along the bottom edge for the adjacent-tread fixing.

Next, glue the tongue-and-groove joint between the riser and nosing and insert the pocket screws. Set the step-shaped riser/nosing into the glued housings of newel and string, up against the glued back-edge of the adjacent tread and insert the two screws at each end, followed by the three screws along the bottom edge. Clean off any excess glue on the face side.

14 The staircase is now ready for fixing. Remove the struts and lower carefully into position. Re-check the newel posts for plumb and check that the staircase is seated properly at top and bottom levels. Fix bottom newel to the floor; fix top newel to the trimmer by skew-nailing through the side (two 75 mm or 100 mm oval nails) or – better still – by pocket screwing; nail nosing to landing trimmer with four floor brads or lost-head nails; then, finally, complete the fixing of the inner string to the wall.

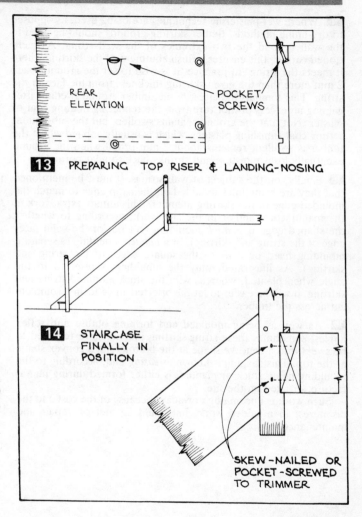

REAR ELEVATION

POCKET SCREWS

13 PREPARING TOP RISER & LANDING-NOSING

14 STAIRCASE FINALLY IN POSITION

SKEW-NAILED OR POCKET-SCREWED TO TRIMMER

15 Where wet-plastering techniques are being used, as opposed to dry-lining methods, timber skirting-grounds should be fixed to the wall beyond the two extremes of the wall string. As mentioned earlier, this ensures a flush abutment of the skirting where it meets the string. In practice, it is wise to set the grounds back 2 mm more than the given skirting thickness from the face of the string. This combats the effect of the timber ground swelling after gaining an excess of moisture from the rendering/floating coat of plaster. Not that the ground remains swollen, but the subsequent setting coat (finishing plaster), which is usually applied whilst the timber is swollen, remains about 2 mm proud when the ground eventually loses moisture and shrinks back to near normal.

16 Finally, on the subject of wall strings, it must be mentioned that they are sometimes moulded on their top edge to match the moulded edge of the skirting member. This entails extra work in the manufacture and/or in the site work, according to whether the shaped edge is a *stuck* moulding (cut out of the solid face-edge of the string and skirting), or a *planted* moulding (a separate moulding fixed by nails to the square edges of the string and skirting). As illustrated, only the moulding is bisected to the angle when planted, whereas with the stuck-moulded string and skirting, it will be easier to let the bisected angle form a complete cut across the timber.

17 As well as being moulded and forming obtuse and reflex angles, sometimes these string/skirting junctions are required to be swept into a concave shape at the bottom and a convex shape at the top. This shaping is known as *easing* and, according to the moulding being stuck or planted, is either formed during manufacture, or fixed on the site.

Such work is uncommon nowadays because of the cost and the disinterest in moulded work, but could be met on repair and maintenance jobs.

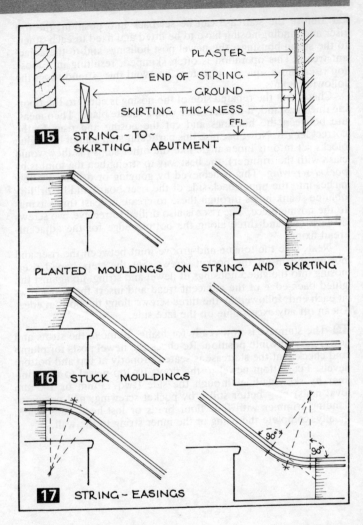

15 STRING-TO-SKIRTING ABUTMENT

PLANTED MOULDINGS ON STRING AND SKIRTING

16 STUCK MOULDINGS

17 STRING-EASINGS

18 Although not usually found in presentday stairs, *carriages* have to be taken into account. Carriages are used, particularly on staircases over 900 mm wide, to give extra support to the steps. They also act as ceiling joists if the sloping soffit is to be boarded or plastered. The timbers of the carriage, usually consisting of three 100 × 75 mm sawn runners, span the underside pitch of the staircase. The central timber is the main carriage, sometimes used without the two outsiders when the underside of the staircase is left open. The outsiders are referred to as rough strings or bearers. The carriage pieces run against the arrises of the steps and are birdsmouthed at the bottom onto a 100 × 50 mm floor plate and at the top against the trimmer joist. Pieces of square-ended and splayed board, ex. 150 × 25 mm, referred to as *rough brackets*, are fixed on alternate sides of the central carriage only, up against the tread and riser of each step.

19 The remaining work on the staircase and stairwell, in most cases, is best left until the second fixing stage, after plastering. This work includes apron linings and nosings, landing handrails and half newels, capping, balusters and newel caps. Even the newels and raking handrail already fixed, would be ideally best left until later, but traditional construction claims these as an integral part of the fitted staircase.

However, they (the fixed newels and handrail) should be protected immediately after installation by being wrapped with kraft or building paper, and/or lagged with thin laths and tied with nylon string or binding wire. If the handrail is of hardwood, it should be coated with a protective lacquer and allowed to dry before being covered.

The treads and risers should also be protected from hard wear and damage for as long as possible during the building operation, by being covered with building paper or a heavy-gauge polythene sheet, held into the shape of the steps by lightly-nailed tread boards.

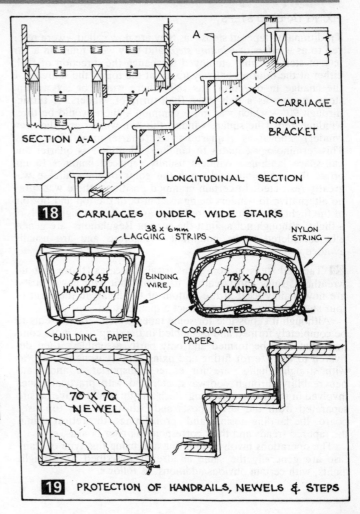

SECTION A-A

LONGITUDINAL SECTION

CARRIAGE

ROUGH BRACKET

18 CARRIAGES UNDER WIDE STAIRS

38 x 6mm LAGGING STRIPS

NYLON STRING

60 x 45 HANDRAIL

BINDING WIRE

78 x 40 HANDRAIL

BUILDING PAPER

CORRUGATED PAPER

70 x 70 NEWEL

19 PROTECTION OF HANDRAILS, NEWELS & STEPS

FIXING TAPERED STEPS

Traditionally, tapered steps – as they are now called – were referred to as *winders* or *winding steps* and they were found in a variety of stair designs, employed to change the direction of flight either at the bottom, halfway up, or at the top of the staircase. If the change in direction was 180°, there would be six winding steps, known as a half-space (half-turn) of winders. If turning through 90° – which was more common – there would be three winding steps (the square winder, the kite winder and the skew winder), known as a quarter-space (quarter-turn) of winders. This terminology equates to landings, identified as quarter and half-space landings. Winders usually replaced landings to improve the headroom and when the going of the staircase was greatly restricted. In certain cramped positions, there was often no alternative to winders being used at both the top and bottom of the flight. However, tapered steps at middle and high levels of a flight, although not against the current Regulations, are generally considered to be potentially dangerous and are usually avoided.

20 Tapered steps in non-geometrical staircases (those without wreathed strings and wreathed handrails, but with newel posts) are now mainly used at the bottom of the flight, in the form of four steps, as illustrated, to effect a quarter-turn.

Although it is possible for some tapered-step arrangements to be completely formed and assembled in the shop, it is more common that they be formed and only partly assembled, then delivered to the site for fitting and fixing. The reasons for this, as with straight flights, are for easier transportation and manoeuvreability through doorways, etc. and with practical issues involved in the fitting and fixing. Such a flight would arrive on site separated from the newel posts and balustrade, the top riser board, the landing nosings and apron linings, the return string, the tapered treads and their corresponding riser boards, etc.

The operations involved in fitting and fixing this type of staircase are generally the same as already described for straight flights, with certain obvious additions, as follows.

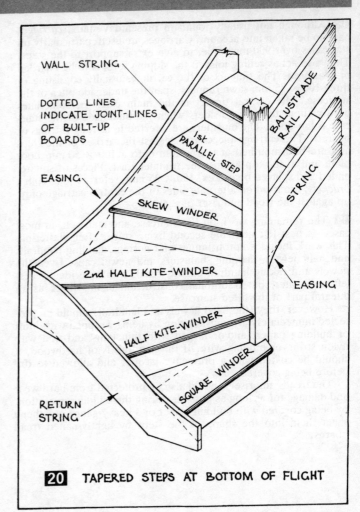

WALL STRING

DOTTED LINES INDICATE JOINT-LINES OF BUILT-UP BOARDS

EASING

1st PARALLEL STEP

SKEW WINDER

BALUSTRADE RAIL

STRING

2nd HALF KITE-WINDER

EASING

HALF KITE-WINDER

SQUARE WINDER

RETURN STRING

20 TAPERED STEPS AT BOTTOM OF FLIGHT

21 First, the main flight is offered up and fitted to the landing above and checked for level and plumb. To achieve this, built-up packing will be required at the bottom to compensate for the four missing tapered steps. Alternatively, two short, timber props can be used, one under the bottom edge of the extended wall string, the other from the underside of the first available tread on the other side. If propped like this, the staircase should remain steady, because the end of the extended wall string butts up to the return wall.

The return string, which connects to the main wall-string with a tongued housing joint, is fitted and tried into position, the tops of the long tread-housings then being checked for level. The two strings ought to be at right angles to each other, but this will depend largely on whether the return wall is truly square or not (which is another reason for assembling and fitting these steps in-situ).

After these initial operations, the staircase will require repositioning to allow for the fitting and fixing of the balustrade. As with the straight flight, this can be done by pushing the staircase up onto the landing and supporting the bottom end with packing and struts. The fitting of the balustrade then follows the sequence of: (a) fix bottom newel post by gluing and pinning to string tenons, (b) insert handrail and balustrade rails (if morticed into newels), (c) glue and fit top newel to handrail, balustrade rails and outer string, (d) quickly complete the pinning of the unpinned joints, (e) fix top riser and landing nosing – after joining same together.

Back into position again, the main flight is re-checked and fixed as previously described. The tongued housing joint is glued and fitted and the return wall-string fixed to the return wall.

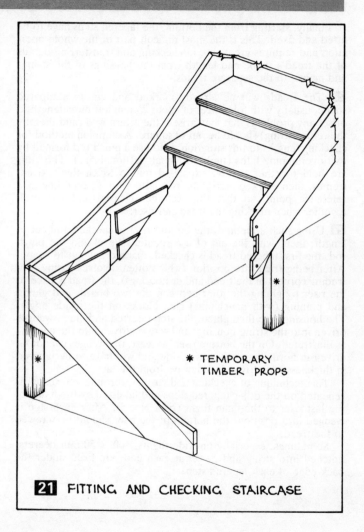

* TEMPORARY TIMBER PROPS

21 FITTING AND CHECKING STAIRCASE

Finally, starting from the bottom, the tapered steps have to be fitted and fixed. This is the most difficult part of the whole operation and requires great care in checking and transferring details of the tread's shape and length from the housings of the strings and newel, to the separate treads.

22 The treads will be already marked and cut to a tapered shape, usually with tolerances of about 25 mm left on in length to offset any problems that may arise if the return wall (and thereby the return string) should be out of square. A common method for checking lengths in this situation, is to use a pinch rod formed by two overlapping laths (timber of small sectional size). The laths are held together tightly, expanded out to touch the two extremes, then marked across the two laths with a pencil line as a reference point, so that they can be released and put back together when marking the tread and riser.

23 Using such a method, the bottom riser is checked and cut to length; then, with the aid of a carpenter's bevel and the pinch rod, the first tapered tread is checked, marked and cut to shape. After being tried into position (which often involves easing protruding corners of the tread and/or housings), the tread is fixed to the riser by gluing the joint between the two boards and gluing and pinning (with panel pins) glue blocks on the inside angle. The housings are then glued, the step inserted and glued-wedges driven into the string-housings and screws driven into the newel – as illustrated. On the bottom riser, at least, the wedges cannot be driven-in normally on the string side and will have to be tapered in thickness and driven-in sideways from the face.

This technique of checking and cutting, forming and fixing, is repeated on the other tapered steps and finalized by the fixing of the last riser to the main flight (riser No. 5). After each step is wedged into position, the bottom of the riser should be screwed to the tread.

Sometimes, especially on wide flights, 100 × 50 mm bearers, notched into string and newel at each end, are fixed under the back edge of each tapered step.

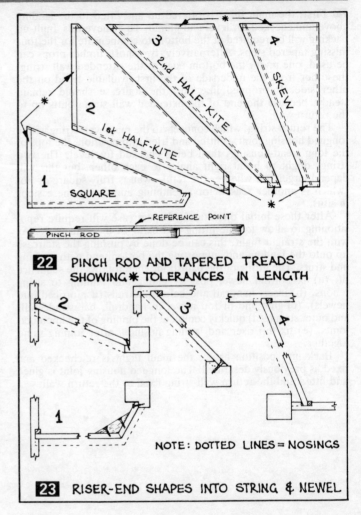

22 PINCH ROD AND TAPERED TREADS SHOWING * TOLERANCES IN LENGTH

NOTE: DOTTED LINES = NOSINGS

23 RISER-END SHAPES INTO STRING & NEWEL

THE BUILDING REGULATIONS, 1976

1 These Regulations came into operation in January 1977 to replace the 1972 Regulations and Amendments. They apply throughout England and Wales apart from the Inner London boroughs, which are covered by the London Building Acts. Part H of these Regulations deals with stairways and balustrades (as well as ramps and vehicle barriers), but, in its complexity, is not easy to follow. In producing a modified and illustrated interpretation of Part H here, covering most of the points concerning stairways and balustrades only, an attempt has been made to present a clearer picture of stair regulations as a guide, but not as a substitute.

In previous Regulations, only dwellings with private stairways and common stairways were referred to, but now all classes of buildings are covered. The classification of these buildings is an important area of study in relation to Part H, and is given in the table to Regulation E2, referred to as the *Designation of purpose groups*. The term *purpose group*, abbreviated throughout here as 'pg', refers to the purpose for which a building is intended to be used. The following definition of the eight purpose groups is only a condensed version of the table to Regulation E2.

pg I =   Residential – private dwelling houses – excluding flats and maisonettes.

pg II =   Institutional – hospitals and other establishments used as living accommodation or dealing with treatment, care or convalescence of disabled, ill, aged, or physically or mentally handicapped.

pg III = Residential – (excluding pg I and pg II) – flats, hotels, halls of residence, etc.

pg IV =   Offices.

pg V =   Shops or shop premises.

pg VI =   Factories (excluding slaughter houses, etc.).

pg VII = Public assembly – buildings used for social, recreational, educational, etc. activities; i.e. dance halls and clubs, sports centres, schools, etc. not already covered in pg I to VI.

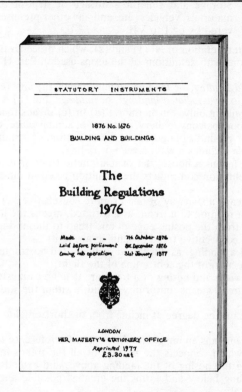

1 THE BUILDING REGULATIONS, with reference to:-
Part H, page 104 to 119, and
Part E, E2, page 58 to 60

pg VIII = Storage and general – storage or deposit of goods, materials, vehicles, etc. and any other premises not covered by pg I to VII.

An interpretation of Hl (1) and (2), which precedes the actual Regulations with definitions of the terms used in Part H, is given here:

Associated landing, or *landing*, as illustrated, (a) and (c) can be referred to as *associated landings*, or *landings*, but (b) is referred to as a *landing* only. Furthermore, (a) or (c) means that portion of any floor, balcony, gallery, platform or similar place, or of any paving or ground situated at the top or bottom of a stairway;

Balustrade includes a wall, screen or railing;

Dwelling means a house, flat or maisonette (note that this overriding definition contradicts the definition given in the E2 table, for pg I);

Flight means a stairway of one or more consecutive steps;

Going, in relation to a tread, as illustrated, means the horizontal distance from the nosing edge of one tread to the nosing edge of the next consecutive tread or landing above it;

Going of a landing, as illustrated, is measured horizontally along the projection of the centre line of the flight;

Length, width and **nosing** of a tread are defined as illustrated;

Parallel tread means uniformity of width within the width of the stairway;

Pitch means the degree of incline from the horizontal to the pitch line;

Pitch line means an imaginary line – used for reference to various rules – which connects the nosings of all the treads in a flight, including the nosing of the landing above, and extends down to the landing below and forms the greatest possible angle to the horizontal;

Rise, as illustrated, means the vertical distance of one unit of the total division of a flight;

Stairway means any part of a building which provides a route of travel from one level to another in the form of one or more flights and intervening landings;

Step does not include any threshold which: (a) has a height not exceeding 40 mm in the case of an internal doorway or 75 mm in the case of an external doorway; or (b) is provided for the purposes of Regulation E18 (6)(c), (which requires a step of not less than 100 mm rise to be a part of any doorway built into a wall between a garage and a house);

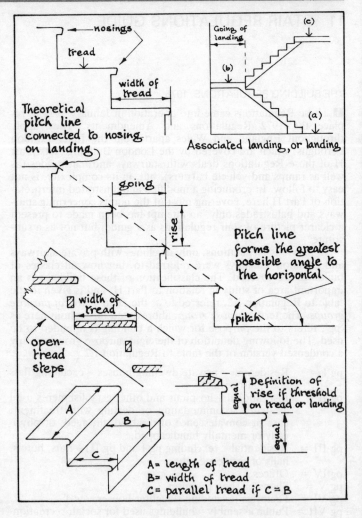

Deemed length. If consecutive tapered treads are of different lengths, each tread shall be deemed to have a length equal to the shortest length of such treads, and *deemed length* shall be construed accordingly (note that as tapered treads create different lengths within the illustrated type of staircase, deemed length is used to gain uniformity for the purpose of defining the extremities to which the pitch lines will refer (see later illustrations);

Tapered tread means a tread greater in width at one side than the other, with a constantly diminishing going throughout its length;

Width, in relation to a stairway, means its unobstructed width, that is to say, clear of handrails and other projections – and, for this purpose, no account shall be taken of any projecting string or skirting not exceeding 30 mm in thickness (note that this definition will effectively increase the structural width of the stairway, as, in the 1972 Regulations, the definition for widths of stairways, according to the width, was either from the wall on one side to the centre line of the handrail on the other, or from the centre line of the handrail on one side to the centre line of the handrail on the other side);

Purpose groups. Any reference to a specified purpose group shall be construed as a reference to the purpose group given in the table to Regulation E2 – and the purpose group of a building shall be determined in accordance with E2 except that, if a building is to be used for more than one purpose, thereby relating to a mixture of purpose groups, it shall be related to the purpose group that attracts the most stringent standards; and

Any stairway or portion of a stairway serving in a building as described above, shall also be related to the purpose group that attracts the most stringent standards.

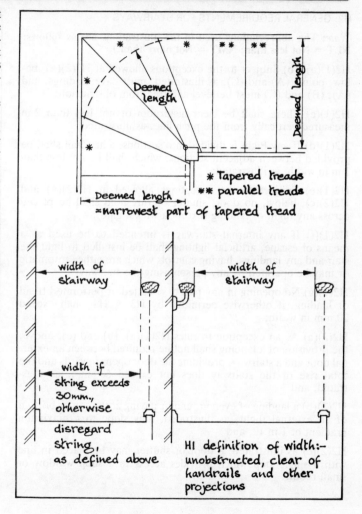

H2: GENERAL REQUIREMENTS FOR STAIRWAYS

(*Note*: **The abbreviations used in the illustrations are as follows: NLT = Not less than; NMT = Not more than.**)

H2(1)(a), (b) Subject to the exceptions allowed at H2(2)(a), below, points (A) and (C), as illustrated, must have landings; and (A), (B) and (C) must be level and free from obstruction;

H2(1)(c) There shall be clear headroom of not less than 2 m measured vertically from the pitch line, as illustrated;

H2(1)(d) If any flight is divided into sections, a handrail shall be provided between adjacent sections, which shall be not less than 1 m in width, as illustrated;

H2(1)(e) Subject to the exceptions allowed at H2(2)(a) and H2(2)(c), below, no door, shutter or threshold shall be placed across any flight or landing (except a wicket gate);

H2(1)(f) If any internal stairway is intended to be used as a means of escape, artificial lighting shall be installed to light the stair and any landings, having controls which are either automatic or may be operated by any person using the stairway;

H2(1)(g) No opening in any part of a slatted or perforated tread or landing, if otherwise permitted by H3 or H4, shall exceed 20 mm in width;

H2(2)(a) As an exception to rules H2(1)(a), (b) and (e), above, the provision of a landing shall not be required between an external door and a stairway, providing the door opens inwards and the total rise of the stairway does not exceed 600 mm, as illustrated; and

H2(2)(b) a landing of even ground or paving at the top or bottom of an external flight, as illustrated, may slope to a maximum gradient of 1 in 12; and

H2(2)(c) as illustrated, a door or shutter may be placed in line with a single step which provides access to a shop window or small room.

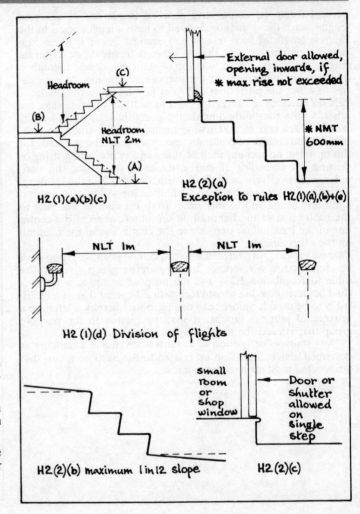

H3: FURTHER REQUIREMENTS FOR STAIRWAYS

H3(2) If a stairway is part of an escape route which passes through a column (4) and a column (5) building (explained on next page), the whole of the stairway must be treated as if belonging to the purpose group that attracts the most stringent standards (i.e. column (4)), if the stairway which attracts the least stringent standards (i.e. column (5)) happens to be closer to the exit.

H3(4) All flights shall be so constructed that:
(a) each step, whether of straight or curved nosing, has either a parallel tread or a tapered tread;
(b) the rise of all steps (subject to H3(6)), below, is uniform in height at any point;
(c) each tread is level;
(d) the width of each tread (in cross-section) is not less than the going measured in plan;
(e) the material length of each tread is not less than the regulation width of the stairway;
(f) as illustrated, there is not less than 15 mm overlap on open-tread steps;
(g) all parallel treads have the same going;
(h) all consecutive tapered treads have the same rate of taper, their narrow ends at one side only (thereby prohibiting a swan-neck change in flight), and the same going measured centrally around the pitch line, as illustrated;
(j) if open-tread stairs are used in buildings of purpose group I or III, or purpose group II used by children under the age of five years, the opening in the rise position, as illustrated, shall not be of such a size as would permit complete entry of a sphere having a diameter of 100 mm.

H3(5) As an exception to the rule at H3(4)(a), above, the bottom step, or two steps, of a flight may be rounded or splayed at one end and/or the other, as illustrated.

H3(6) As an exception to the rule at H3(4)(b), above, steps with a non-uniform rise are allowed at the top or bottom of a flight joining ground or paving outside a building, if the rise measurement at the centre of such steps, as illustrated, is equal to all the other rises in the flight.

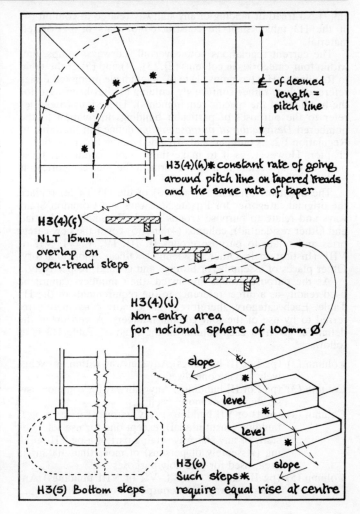

℄ of deemed length = pitch line

H3(4)(h)* constant rate of going around pitch line on tapered treads and the same rate of taper

H3(4)(ƒ)
NLT 15mm overlap on open-tread steps

H3(4)(j)
Non-entry area for notional sphere of 100mm Ø

slope

level

level

slope

H3(6)
Such steps* require equal rise at centre

H3(5) Bottom steps

H3(7) No tread or landing of any stairway related to column (4) of the H3 table, shall be constructed of slats or perforated material.

The current regulations now cover all stairways, ramps, etc. within four categories in columns (2), (3), (4) and (5) of the table to Regulation H3; (columns (1) to (4) might have promoted easier reference, but, rather confusingly, column (1) has been used for the headings of the specific requirements). These four categories refer to the purposes of particular buildings in relation to the numbered *Designation of purpose groups* defined in the table to Regulation E2, as outlined and explained on the first page of this chapter. However, as if to make things more confusing, these purpose groups relate in a mixed form to the four categories, as explained below.

The first two, columns (2) and (3) of the H3 Table, replace the original categories for Private Stairways and Common Stairways and relate to purpose groups I and III (Small residential; and Other residential); columns (4) and (5) cover the new categories and relate to purpose groups II, III, IV, V, VI, VII or VIII (Institutional; Other residential; Office; Shop; Factory; Other places of assembly; or Storage and general, respectively).

As the purpose groups are mixed, their numbers cannot be used readily as a direct reference to the requirements of the H3 Table. Each category, therefore, will be more conveniently referred to by use of the four column numbers. A version of the definition given in each column at the head of Table H3 is as follows:

Column (2) (pg I or III buildings) Any stairway within or exclusively serving one dwelling.

Column (3) (pg I or III buildings) Any stairway for common use, serving two or more dwellings.

Column (4) (pg II or VII buildings) Any stairway serving a pg II building (Institutional), except one for use solely by staff; or any stairway serving part of a pg VII building (Assembly of persons) of more than 100 m² in area, used for assembly purposes.

Column (5) (pg II, III, IV, V, VI, VII or VIII buildings) Any other stairway in any purpose group except pg I.

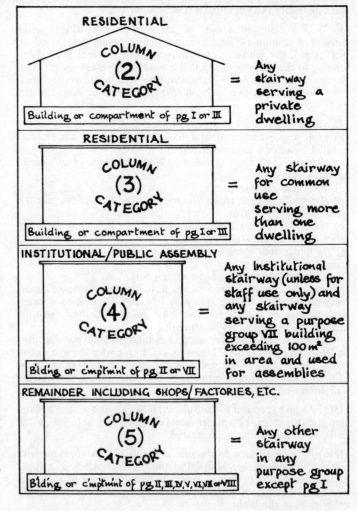

TABLE TO REGULATION H3: SPECIFIC REQUIREMENTS FOR STAIRWAYS

Column (2) requirements

A Width of stairway (subject to the provisions of Section II of Part E, Means of escape in case of fire):

(a) Not less than 600 mm when a staircase provides access only to one room, not being a living-room or kitchen, or to a bathroom and/or a W.C.

(b) Not less than 800 mm normally. (Note that the regulation width-of-stairway, in the example shown, is between the wall's finished surface and the inner face of the newel post, whereas the joinery width for a staircase is between the outer faces of the strings, and the carpentry width is over-all (O/A), i.e. from outer face of wall string to outer face of newel post.)

B The additional requirement for stairways over 1.8 m in width does not apply.

C Pitch of flight to be not more than 42°.

D Except at the foot of a stairway, not less than two nor more than sixteen rises per flight; this does not apply to any step giving access to a dais, stage, shop window, small room or an external doorway.

E Rise of a step to be not less than 75 mm nor more than 220 mm.

F Going of a step to be not less than 220 mm.

G The sum of the going plus twice the rise of a step (traditionally known as 2R + G) to be not less than 550 mm nor more than 700 mm (subject to the criteria laid down for tapered treads). This shall not apply to a flight with only one rise.

H Going of landings (subject to Section II of Part E, Means of escape in case of fire) to be not less than the width of the stairway.

Table to Regulation H6 (combined with H3 : K):

H6 ② A balustrade guarding a flight which is within a dwelling or serving only one dwelling, shall be not less than 840 mm nor more than 1 m (measured vertically above the pitch line); and ④ A balustrade guarding a landing or floor in the same situation as above, shall be not less than 900 mm from the finished floor surface.

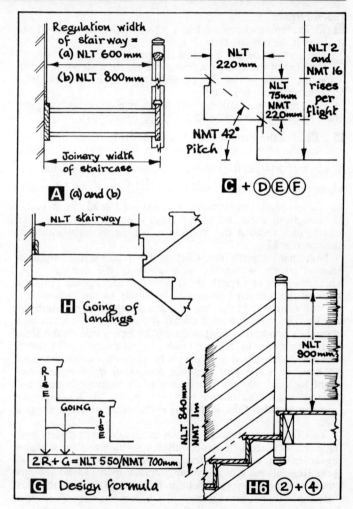

Regulation width of stairway =
(a) NLT 600mm
(b) NLT 800mm

Joinery width of staircase

A (a) and (b)

NLT 220mm

NLT 75mm NMT 220mm

NMT 42° Pitch

NLT 2 and NMT 16 rises per flight

C + **D** **E** **F**

NLT stairway

H Going of landings

RISE

GOING

RISE

2R + G = NLT 550/NMT 700mm

G Design formula

NLT 900mm

NLT 840mm NMT 1m

H6 ② + ④

Tapered treads

J (a) The going of any part of a tread within the width of the stairway to be not less than 75 mm;

(b) The going to be not less than 220 mm;

(c) The sum of the going plus twice the rise of a step (2R + G), being the same as that for parallel steps, to be not less than 550 mm nor more than 700 mm;

(d) The pitch, in relation to the defined position of the pitch lines, to be not more than 42°.

1 & **2** For the purposes of (b), (c) and (d) above, the going, the rise and the pitch must be measured at the central points of the tread's length $\left(\frac{L}{2}\right)$ in the radial path depicted by the pitch line, or, where applicable, the deemed length $\left(\frac{DL}{2}\right)$ of a tread if the stairway is less than 1 m in width, as illustrated at **1**; or at points 270 mm from each end of the tread's length, or the deemed length, of a tread if the stairway is 1 m or more in width, as illustrated at **2**.

Note that the pitch lines relate to the tread's actual length, or deemed length, within the inner width of the stairway – but whether one or two (pitch lines) are required, depends upon the width of the stairway between the handrails, or the handrail and the wall's surface. In the case of tapered steps, two handrails are required, in effect, on all stairways (Regulation H3 : K) if, as is normal, a handrail is designated on the newel-side of the stair-case. Therefore, to be just inside the Regulations, the actual stair-width calculation must always be: minimum width (600 mm, 800 mm, or 1 m), plus handrail projection from wall (which might be, say, 100 mm, depending upon handrail bracket and handrail size), plus plaster thickness, equals the measurement from the outside of the wall string to the inside of the newel-post line.

Tapered steps, although visually attractive, have always been regarded as potentially dangerous and so the need for stringent regulations can be appreciated. However, the combined effect of these Regulations, which overlap, interact upon and modify each other, now make it very difficult to fit tapered steps into the illustrated, traditional arrangement of a square, quarter-space turn. In fact, from a strict technical definition, it is only possible on stairways that qualify for a single, central pitch line, as illustrated and explained on the next page.

To test the interaction of the various regulations on quarter-turn, tapered steps, within the confines of a non-geometrical

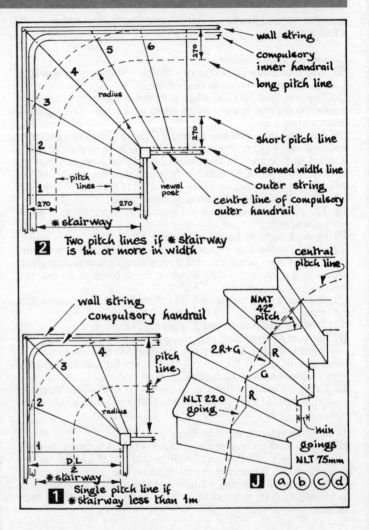

staircase, the following examples have been worked out separately on a large-scale drawing before being reproduced here. It was found that because of the introduction, in these latest Regulations, of the single, central pitch line for stairways less than 1 m wide, the old arrangement of three winders (square, kite and skew) could be revived quite successfully – in a modified form, of course, not radiating from the centre of the newel like its predecessors. Other step-arrangements with a central pitch line also worked out successfully, but when double pitch lines were used on the wider stairway examples of 1 m or more, violations regarding uniform goings around the long pitch lines were unavoidable in all cases. Three-tread and four-tread arrangements failed 2R + G and a five-tread contained more going violations than a six-tread arrangement.

The reason for this is that as the quadrantal pitch lines in the illustrations must radiate from the corner of the newel post at (a) and the tapered treads – to achieve minimum goings – must radiate from points beyond the newel at (b), the goings in these arrangements cannot be tangential to the central geometrical normal of any sector shape thus formed by such steps (see separated tread No. 4). Thereby, irregular goings are created across the different positioned treads, even though the same rate of taper exists. This can be overcome when only one pitch line is used, but not with two, unless the rate of taper is tampered with – yet another violation.

Six tread/double pitch line

3 This example, scaled to a regulation stairway width of 1 m between handrail and newel post, which demands two pitch lines, can be set out by the following method: draw basic outline of stairway, establish pitch lines and the nosing line at 45° from the corner of the newel post; where nosing line cuts short pitch line, set out three steps on either side along the pitch line with dividers set at 220 mm; from the first nosing line on the horizontal, radiate angles of 15°, 30°, 60°, 75° and 90°, through the points on the short pitch line. Check uniformity of going on the long pitch line (note marginal violations here); check 2R + G on both pitch lines; check pitch angle. In this example, the working out is: 550 – G(220) = 330 ÷ 2 = 165 mm minimum rise (which must be checked on the long pitch line, i.e. 165 × 2 = 330 + 367 = 697 mm, which is within the 2R + G rule), and 700 – G(367) = 333 ÷ 2 = 166.5 mm maximum rise (which must be checked on the short pitch line, i.e. 166.5 × 2 = 333 + 220 going = 553 mm, which is also within the 2R + G rule).

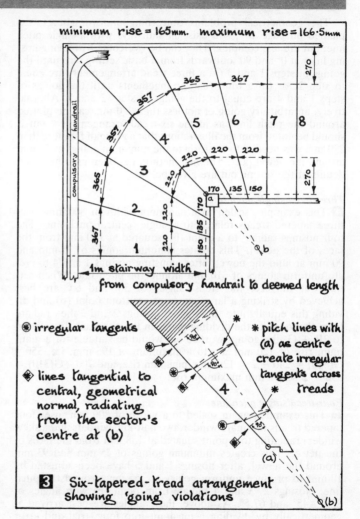

minimum rise = 165mm. maximum rise = 166·5mm

1m stairway width

from compulsory handrail to deemed length

⊛ irregular tangents

❖ lines tangential to central, geometrical normal, radiating from the sector's centre at (b)

✳ pitch lines with (a) as centre create irregular tangents across treads

3 Six-tapered-tread arrangement showing 'going' violations

The geometrical problems concerning uniform goings, explained on page 107, still exist on stairways with a single pitch line, but are less complex. They can be overcome by moving nosing lines at 0° and 90° outwards from a basic setting out, until the goings of steps 1 and 3 (in a three-tread arrangement) are equal to step 2, or (in a four-tread arrangement) until the goings of steps 1 and 4 are equal to the goings of steps 2 and 3. Alternatively, an arbitrary going of not less than 220 mm can be plotted around the pitch line, as in the six-tread arrangement – but it should be noted from the illustrations that a going of far more than 220 mm was needed to conform to the minimum goings of 75 mm around the newel post. The first method has been used here and details of the setting out are given below.

Three-tread/single pitch line

4 This example, scaled to a minimum width of 800 mm, uses three tapered treads related to a single, central pitch line. The four nosings radiate to a point (b), squared at 120 mm from the faces of the newel. This creates minimum goings of 75 mm and 90 mm around the newel, after adjusting nosings 1 and 4 to create uniform goings of 310 mm around the pitch line. When setting out full-size, the steps' angles of 30° and 60° are best achieved by striking a large quadrant arc from point (b) and dividing this equally into three parts; nosings 2 and 3 then radiate from (b) to strike the dividing points in the quadrant. In relation to 2R + G, the goings worked out would be suitable for a minimum rise of 120 mm, up to a maximum of 195 mm, i.e. 550 – G(310) = 240 ÷ 2 = 120 mm minimum rise, and 700 – G(310) = 390 ÷ 2 = 195 mm maximum rise.

Four-tread/single pitch line

5 This example, again scaled to a width of 800 mm, uses four tapered treads (a square winder, two half-kite winders and a skew winder) radiating to a point squared at 158 mm from the faces of the newel. This creates minimum goings of 75 mm and 93 mm around the newel, after nosings 1 and 5 have been adjusted by 10 mm to produce uniform goings of 255 mm around the pitch line. Nosings 2, 3 and 4 radiate from point (b) with angles of 22.5°, 45° and 67.5°. As above, these angles are best arrived at geometrically by dividing a quadrant into four, trial and error method, by stepping of dividers or a trammel compass around the quadrant's path. In relation to 2R + G, the going of 255 mm would be suitable for a minimum rise of 147.5 mm, up to a max-

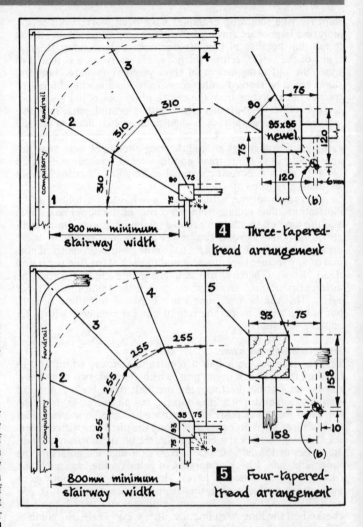

4 Three-tapered-tread arrangement

5 Four-tapered-tread arrangement

imum of 220 mm, i.e. 550 − G(255) = 295 ÷ 2 = 147.5 mm minimum rise, and 700 − G (255) = 445 ÷ 2 = 222.5 mm rise. This second calculation fails the regulation rise and, therefore, is brought down to 220 mm. This gives a maximum pitch of approximately 41°.

Column (3) requirements
A Width of stairway (subject to the provisions of Section II of part E, Means of escape in case of fire):
Not less than 900 mm. (Note that the regulation width-of-stairway, in the example shown, is between the wall's finished surface and the inner edge of the handrail, unless some other part projects further into the stairway, whereas the formwork width for concrete is from the wall to the outer edge of the steps.)
B The additional requirement for stairways over 1.8 m in width does not apply.
C Pitch of flight to be not more than 38°.
Ⓓ Not less than two nor more than sixteen rises per flight; this does not apply to any step giving access to a dais, stage, shop window, small room or an external doorway.
Ⓔ Rise of a step to be not less than 75 mm nor more than 190 mm.
Ⓕ Going of a step to be not less than 240 mm.
G The sum of the going plus twice the rise of a step (2R + G) to be not less than 550 mm nor more than 700 mm (subject to the criteria laid down for tapered treads). This shall not apply to a flight with only one rise.
H Going of landings (subject to Section II of Part E, Means of escape in case of fire) to be not less than the width of the stairway.

Table to Regulation H6 (combined with H3 : K):
H6 Ⓒ A balustrade guarding a flight within or serving a column (3) building, shall be not less than 900 mm nor more than 1 m (measured vertically above the pitch line); and
Ⓔ A balustrade guarding a landing or floor in the same situation as above, shall be not less than 1.1 m from the finished floor surface.

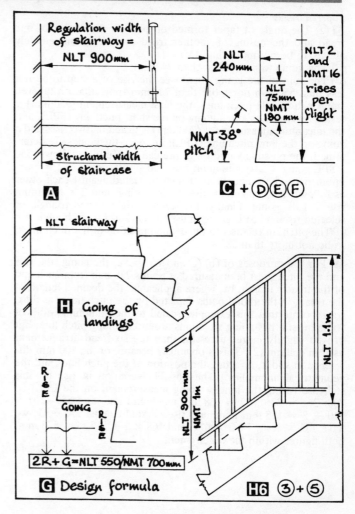

Tapered treads

J (a) The angle of taper formed on plan by the nosing of one tread and the nosing of another tread or landing immediately above, to be not more than 15°;

(b) The going to be not less than 240 mm;

(c) The sum of the going plus twice the rise of a step to be not less than 550 mm nor more than 700 mm (note that on tapered steps with double pitch lines, the least measurement (550 mm) is tested on two rises and a going on the short pitch line (SPL), and the maximum measurement (700 mm) is tested on two rises and a going on the long pitch line (LPL); i.e. once the goings are determined, the possible variation in rise can be found as follows: 550 – SPL going ÷ 2 = minimum rise; 700 – LPL going ÷ 2 = maximum rise. These figures must then be tested against each other as follows: 2 × maximum rise + SPL going, and 2 × minimum rise + LPL going. Finally, the steepest right-angled triangle of selected rise and SPL going, must be checked for pitch angle);

(d) The pitch, in relation to the defined position of the pitch lines, to be not more than 38°.

1 For the purposes of (b), (c) and (d) above, the going, the rise and the pitch must be measured at points 270 mm from each end of the tread's length, or, where applicable, the deemed length of the tread, in the radial paths depicted by the pitch lines, as illustrated (note that this example, scaled to the minimum width of 900 mm, still has going violations around the long pitch line, but proved slightly more successful than the six-tread arrangement used in column (2). This is obviously because of the 100 mm difference in width, affecting the position of the pitch lines and the geometrical anomalies.) The possible variation in rise on this staircase (using the longest going measurement on the LPL) is: 700 − 364 = 336 ÷ 2 = 168 mm maximum rise, and 550 − 240 = 310 ÷ 2 = 155 mm minimum rise. Tested against 2R + G, we have 155 × 2 + LPLG = 674, and 168 × 2 + SPLG = 576 mm, both figures within the requirement.

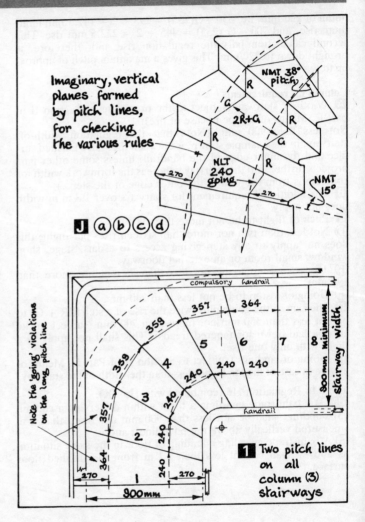

Imaginary, vertical planes formed by pitch lines, for checking the various rules

J (a)(b)(c)(d)

NMT 38° pitch

R   G

2R+G   R   G

R   R

NLT 240 going

NMT 15°

1 Two pitch lines on all column (3) stairways

compulsory handrail

Note the 'going' violations on the long pitch line

357   364

359   5   6   7   8

359   4   240   240

357   3   240

900 mm minimum stairway width

handrail

2   240

364   240

270   1   270

900mm

Column (4) requirements

A Width of stairway (subject to the provisions of Section II of Part E, Means of escape in case of fire):

Not less than 1 m (Note that because the regulation width of a stairway is defined in H1(1) as being clear of obstructions such as handrails, then the initial structural width of the stairway, if concerned with minimum requirements, must be carefully worked out to include the space required for handrails on both sides.)

B Additional requirement for stairways over 1.8 m in width: Such flights must be divided so that each division is:

(a) Not less than 1 m nor more than 1.8 m in width; and

(b) each division shall be separated from the other by a handrail complying with the requirements set out in H3 : K.

C Pitch of flight – no pitch given, but other obviously limiting rules compensate for this omission.

Ⓓ Not less than three nor more than sixteen rises per flight; this does not apply to any step giving access to a dais, stage, shop window, small room or an external doorway.

Ⓔ Rise of a step to be not less than 75 mm nor more than 180 mm.

Ⓕ Going of a step to be not less than 280 mm.

G The sum of the going plus twice the rise of a step (2R + G) to be not less than 550 mm nor more than 700 mm (subject to the criteria laid down for tapered treads). This shall not apply to a flight with only one rise.

H Going of landings (subject to Section II of Part E, Means of escape in case of fire) to be not less than the width of the stairway, or, if the stairway is divided, the width of the widest division (note that if projecting handrails continue around the landing, then, as with stairways, this would have to be taken into account).

Table to Regulation H6 (combined with H3 : K):

H6 ① A balustrade, including any superimposed padded rest, which guards a balcony in a pg VII building and is immediately in front of fixed seating, shall be not less than 790 mm from the finished floor surface.

③ A balustrade guarding a flight within or serving a column (5) building, shall be not less than 900 mm or not more than 1 m (measured vertically above the pitch line); and

⑤ A balustrade guarding a landing or floor in the same situation as above, shall be not less than 1.1 m from the finished floor surface.

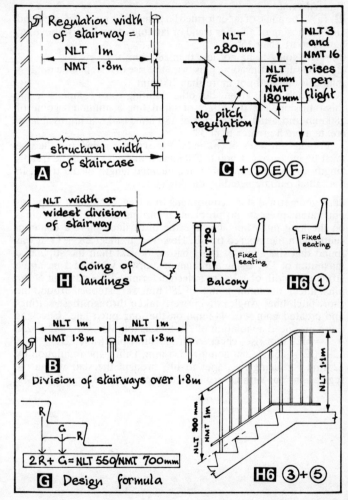

Tapered treads

J (a) The angle of taper formed on plan by the nosing of one tread and the nosing of another tread or landing immediately above, to be not more than 15°;

(b) The going to be not less than 280 mm;

(c) The sum of the going plus twice the rise of a step to be not less than 550 mm and not more than 700 mm.

No pitch angle given, but other limiting rules compensate for this omission, i.e. the effect of stipulating a minimum going of 280 mm and a maximum rise of 180 mm, make it impossible to create a pitch greater than 33°.

For the purposes of (b) and (c) above, the going and the rise must be measured at points 270 mm from each end of the tread's length, or, where applicable, the deemed length of the tread, in the radial path depicted by the pitch lines.

1 A geometrical stair, conforming to a true, segmental shape, as illustrated, presents no problems regarding uniformity of goings on the long pitch line, because the pitch lines share a common centre with the tapered treads. However, to meet 2R + G, it was found that the angle of taper had to be less than the stipulated maximum of 15°. Using a minimum stairway width of 1 m, and a structural width of 1.160 m (which determined the position of the pitch lines), minimum goings of 280 mm were stepped around the short pitch line. Angles of 15° were taken through these settings and created goings of 442 mm on the long pitch line. Checking these produced a violation of 2R + G as follows: 700 − 442 = 258 ÷ 2 = 129 mm rise; checked on the short pitch line, 2R + G = 129 × 2 = 258 + 280 going = 538 mm, failing the regulation by 12 mm. Reducing the taper to 14°, brought the stair within the regulation, but with a very limited step rise of 135 mm.

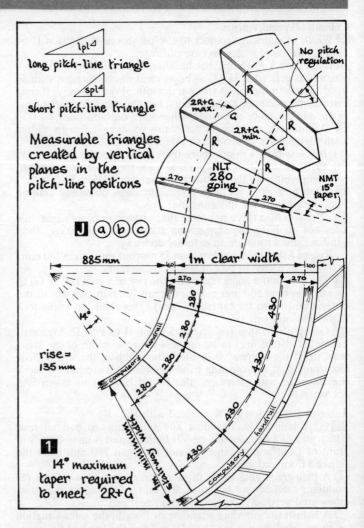

Column (5) requirements

A Width of stairway (subject to the provisions of Section II of Part E, Means of escape in case of fire):

(a) Not less than 800 mm in the case of a stairway within or serving any part of a building which is not capable of being used or occupied by more than fifty persons; or

(b) Not less than 1 m in any other case.

B Additional requirement for stairways over 1.8 m in width: Such flights must be divided so that each division is:

(a) Not less than 1 m, nor more than 1.8 m in width; and

(b) each division shall be separated from the other by a handrail complying with the requirements set out in H3 : K.

C Pitch of flight – no pitch given, but other obviously limiting rules compensate for this omission.

D Not less than three or not more than sixteen rises per flight; this does not apply to any step giving access to a dais, stage, shop window, small room or an external doorway.

E Rise of a step to be not less than 75 mm or not more than 190 mm.

F Going of a step to be not less than 250 mm.

G The sum of the going plus twice the rise of a step (2R + G) to be not less than 550 mm nor more than 700 mm (subject to the criteria laid down for tapered treads). This shall not apply to a flight with only one rise.

H Going of landings (subject to Section II of Part E, Means of escape in case of fire) to be not less than the width of the stairway, or, if the stairway is divided, the width of the widest division (note that if projecting handrails continue around the landing, then, as with stairways, this would have to be taken into account).

Table to Regulation H6 (combined with H3 : K):

H6 ① A balustrade, including any superimposed padded rest, which guards a balcony in a pg VII building and is immediately in front of fixed seating, shall be not less than 790 mm from the finished floor surface.

③ A balustrade guarding a flight within or serving a column (5) building, shall be not less than 900 mm or not more than 1 m (measured vertically above the pitch line); and

⑤ A balustrade guarding a landing or floor in the same situation as above, shall be not less than 1.1 m from the finished floor surface.

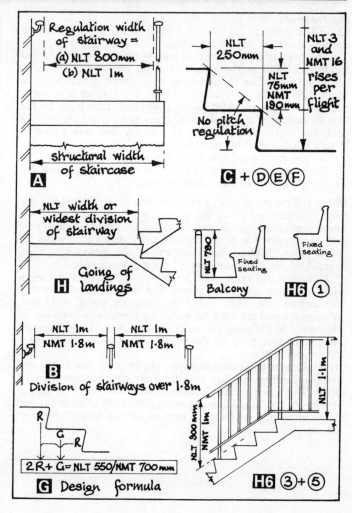

Tapered treads

J (a) The going of any part of a tread within the width of the stairway to be not less than 75 mm;
(b) The angle of taper formed on plan by the nosing of one tread and the nosing of another tread or landing immediately above, to be: (i) not more than 15° in the case of a stairway 1 m or more in width; and (ii) of no specific angle in the case of a stairway 800 mm or more in width (being controlled, therefore, by the limiting factors of rise and going, measured around the central pitch line in relation to 2R + G, and the minimum going of 75 mm at the end of the narrow taper);
(c) The going to be not less than 250 mm;
(d) The sum of the going plus twice the rise of a step to be not less than 550 mm nor more than 700 mm.

1 For the purposes of (c) and (d) above, the going and the rise must be measured (i) at the central points of the length, or, where applicable, the deemed length of the tread, in the radial path of the pitch line, if the stairway is less than 1 m in width, or (ii) at points 270 mm from each end of the tread's length, or deemed length, if the stairway is 1 m or more in width;
(i) This tread was drawn with a taper of 22.5°, scaled to a minimum regulation width of 800 mm, plus the necessary allowance for handrail. The angle suited the minimum going of 75 mm, although it could not have been increased much more without an adjustment to the going on the pitch line. 2R + G and the maximum rise stipulation, set the possible variation in rise between 150 mm and 190 mm.
(ii) This geometrical stair example, like the one used in the column (4) requirements, had to suffer a reduction in taper from 15° to 14°. This was to avoid violation of 2R + G. The difference of 30 mm on the short pitch-line goings, between column (4) and (5) requirements, enabled an increase of rise from 135 mm to 150 mm.

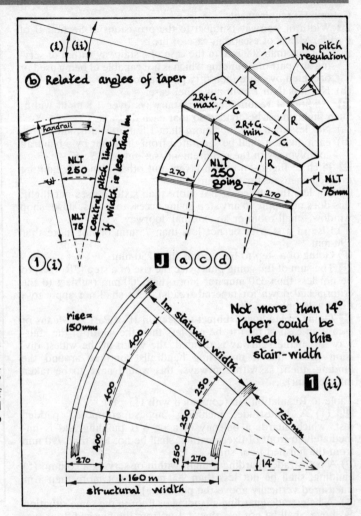

Handrails

These regulations apply to all purpose groups in columns (2), (3), (4) and (5), but do not apply to any side of a flight formed by fixed seating. For easier reference, the details given here, from H3 : K, have been joined with relevant details from H6, concerning guarding of stairways and landings, etc.

K (a) No handrail is required on flights up to 600 mm total rise, but when the rise of a flight exceeds this, handrails are required as follows:

(i) on each side of the flight if the width of the flight is 1 m or more;

(ii) on the side where tapered treads have the greater going (this being normally the side against the structural wall, means that a balustrade on the outer string side will result in two handrails) if the flight is less than 1 m in width and contains tapered treads; and

(iii) on at least one side in any other flight; and

(b) Any handrail shall:

(i) be so designed as to afford adequate means of support to persons using the flight;

(ii) be continuous for the length of the flight (except that any handrail need not extend beside the two steps at the foot of a stairway);

(iii) be securely fixed at a height conforming to the regulations given here separately for each column group (measured vertically above the pitch line); and

(iv) be terminated by a scroll or other suitable means.

H6(1)(a)(b)(i)(ii)(iii) A balustrade shall be provided at each side of any flight and at the perimeter of any landing or floor, or, in places where persons have access for purposes other than maintenance or repair, any part of a balcony, platform, roof, vehicle park, rooflight, etc.

H6(2)(b)(c) The balustrade must be so constructed to be capable of resisting the appropriate load specified in Table 3 of CP3 (Codes of Practice 3) : Chapter V : Part 1 : 1967; and if any part of the balustrade is glazed, it shall be formed of glass blocks, toughened glass or laminated safety glass.

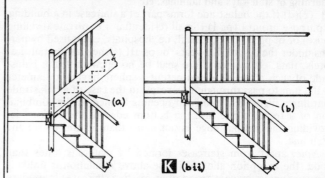

K (bii)

The old practice of terminating handrails (a) on the underside of the upper string in dog-legged flights or (b) against the underside of the stairwell apron-lining, violates K(b)(ii)

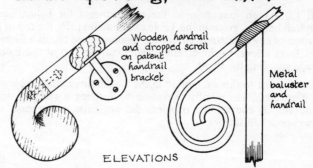

Wooden handrail and dropped scroll on patent handrail bracket

Metal baluster and handrail

ELEVATIONS

K (b)(iv) Handrails fixed to walls, or not terminating into newel posts, must be safely blunted with a scroll or other suitable shape

Guarding of stairways and landings, etc

H6 (2)(d) If the balustrade forms part of a staircase in a building of purpose group I (pg I) (Small residential, i.e. private dwelling house) or of pg II (Institutional, i.e. hospitals, etc.), used by persons under the age of five years, or pg III (Other residential, i.e. hotels, flats, etc.), then there shall be no opening in the balustrade of such a size as would permit a sphere having a diameter of 100 mm to pass through it – except, in the case of a balustrade guarding a flight, any triangular opening formed by the combination of a tread, a rise and the bottom edge of the balustrade, providing the bottom edge is not more than 50 mm above the pitch line.

Note: apart from staircases formed by materials other than wood, the exception allowed in the above regulation is unlikely to occur (unless by conversion of an existing staircase) in modern buildings, where such triangular openings in wooden stairs (in the form of *cut strings*) are obsolete and would almost certainly be filled with vertical balusters, anyway, instead of balustrade rails between newel posts.

H6 (3) As an exception to the requirements for balustrade/handrail heights, given in the Table to Regulation H6, the top of a portion of any balustrade guarding a landing at the top of a flight, may form a level-to-slope reflex angle with the top of the balustrade guarding the flight.

Note: prior to this exemption in the Regulations, this problem, as illustrated, was usually overcome by forming a ramp in the handrail. Of course, the problem did not exist in the case of newel-post balustrades.

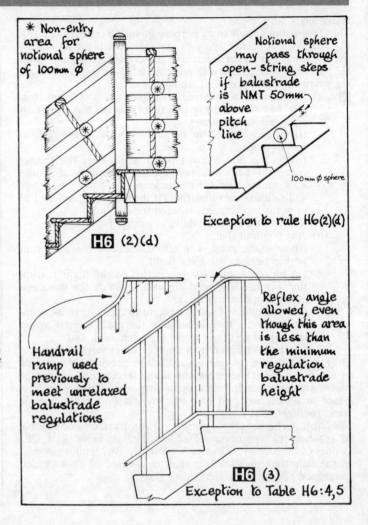

* Non-entry area for notional sphere of 100mm ∅

H6 (2)(d)

Notional sphere may pass through open-string steps if balustrade is NMT 50mm above pitch line

100mm ∅ sphere

Exception to rule H6(2)(d)

Handrail ramp used previously to meet unrelaxed balustrade regulations

Reflex angle allowed, even though this area is less than the minimum regulation balustrade height

H6 (3)
Exception to Table H6:4,5

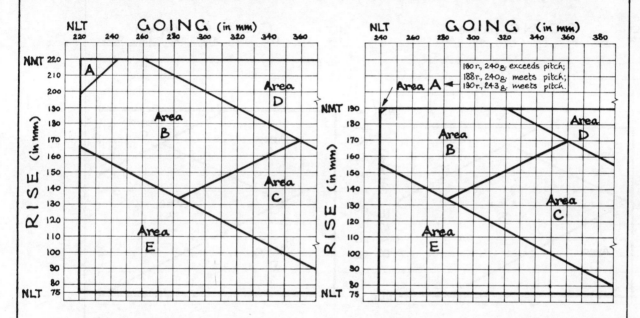

These graphs test the legality of various permutations in rise and going, as follows:-

Area 'A' meets the permitted rise and going, but violates the maximum pitch allowance.
Area 'B': the ratio of any rise and going within this area meets the various regulations.
Area 'C' meets the regulations, but violates the traditionally established minimum pitch of 25°.

Area 'D' violates the maximum of 2R+G (700mm).
Area 'E' violates the minimum of 2R+G (550mm).

COLUMN (4) STAIRWAYS

COLUMN (5) STAIRWAYS

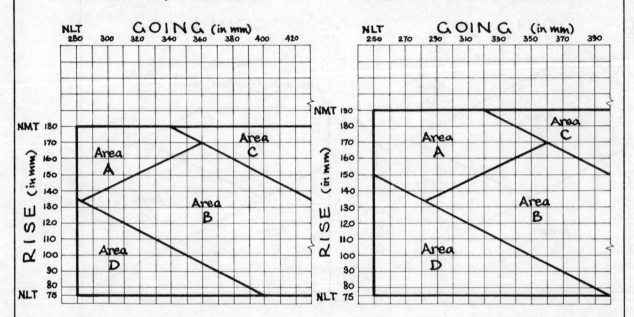

These graphs test the legality of various permutations in rise and going, as follows:-

Area 'A': the ratio of any rise and going within this area meets the various regulations.
Area 'B' meets the regulations, but violates the traditionally established minimum pitch of 25°.

Area 'C' violates the maximum of 2R+G (700mm).
Area 'D' violates the minimum of 2R+G (550mm).

12 CONSTRUCTING FLAT AND PITCHED ROOFS

Roofing in its entirety is an enormous subject, but the practical issues that involve the first-fixing carpenter on the most common types of dwelling-house roof – dealt with here – are less formidable.

TYPES OF ROOF

1 Timber is used for the skeleton structure of the roof and according to its design, whether conforming to a *flat, lean-to* or *pitched roof*, is covered with boards or sheet boarding and impervious materials such as bituminous felt in built-up layers (flat roofs), quarried or asbestos-cement slates, tiles of clay or concrete on sarking felt and battens (pitched and lean-to roofs). Materials such as lead, zinc and copper are now virtually obsolete on flat roofs.

Roofing carpenters nowadays require: (a) a knowledge of both modern and traditional roof construction; and (b) a sound knowledge of at least one of the various methods used for finding lengths and bevels of roofing members. The various methods dealt with later, include geometry, steel roofing-square, metric rafter square, templates and Roofing Ready Reckoner.

Traditional roofing consists basically of rafters pitched up from wall plates to a ridge board, such rafters being supported by purlins and struts which transfer the load to either straining pieces or binders and ceiling joists to an internal load-bearing wall.

Modern roofing, using trussed-rafter assemblies, often uses smaller sectional-sized timbers, only requires (normally) to be supported at the ends, thus freeing the designer from the need to provide intermediate walls, and dispenses with purlins and ridge boards. Other differences are that traditional roofing is usually an entire site operation, whereas trussed-rafter roofing involves prefabrication under factory conditions and delivery of assembled units to the site for a much-reduced site-fixing operation.

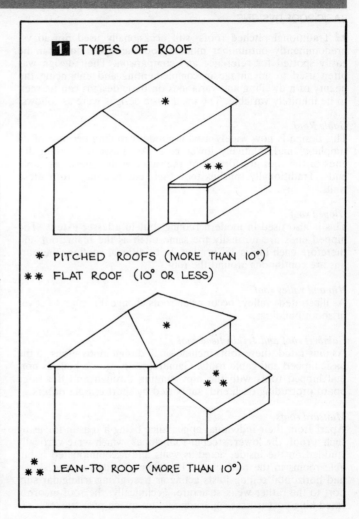

1 TYPES OF ROOF

* PITCHED ROOFS (MORE THAN 10°)
** FLAT ROOF (10° OR LESS)

** LEAN-TO ROOF (MORE THAN 10°)

BASIC ROOF DESIGNS

2 Traditional pitched roofs, still occasionally used nowadays, predominantly outnumber modern roofs and therefore can be easily spotted for reference and comparison. Their design was often used to advantage in complementing and enhancing the beauty of a dwelling and variations on basic designs can be seen to be infinitely variable. The main basic designs were as follows.

Gable Roof
This design is now widely used in modern roofing because of its simplicity and relatively lower cost. As illustrated, triangular ends of the roof are formed by the outer walls, known as gable ends. Traditionally, purlins took their end-bearings from these walls.

Hipped roof
This is also used in modern roofing, but to a lesser extent. The hipped ends are normally the same pitch as the main roof and therefore each hip is 45° in plan. In traditional roofing, the purlins are continuous around the roof.

Hip and valley roof
As illustrated, valleys occur when roofs change direction to cover offshoot buildings.

Gambrel roof and Jerkin-head roof
As illustrated, these roofs include small design innovations to the basic hipped and gable roofs. Gambrel roofs can be built as normal hipped roofs with the hips running through and the ridge board protruding each end, supported by short cripple rafters.

Mansard roofs
Apart from their individual appearance being a reason for using such a roof, the lower, steeper roof-slopes, which were vertically studded on the inside, acted as walls and accommodated habitable rooms in the roof space. The upper, shallower roof slopes had horizontal ceiling joists acting as ties, giving triangular support to the rather weak structure. Technically, the roof incorporated king-post trusses superimposed on queen-post trusses.

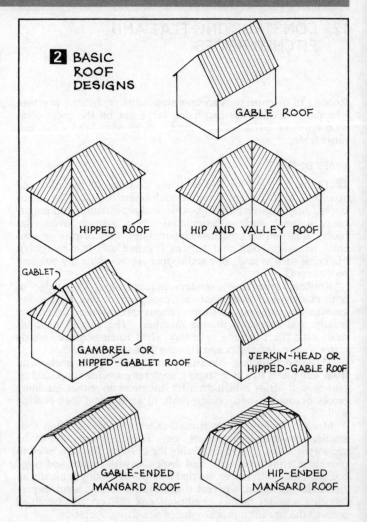

2 BASIC ROOF DESIGNS

GABLE ROOF

HIPPED ROOF

HIP AND VALLEY ROOF

GABLET

GAMBREL OR HIPPED-GABLET ROOF

JERKIN-HEAD OR HIPPED-GABLE ROOF

GABLE-ENDED MANSARD ROOF

HIP-ENDED MANSARD ROOF

ROOF COMPONENTS AND TERMINOLOGY

3 *Wall plates*: 100 × 75 mm or 100 × 50 mm sawn timber bearing plates, laid flat and bedded on mortar to a level position, flush to the inside of the inner wall and running along the wall to carry the feet of all the rafters and the ceiling joists. Nowadays, the wall plates must be anchored down with restraint straps.

Restraint straps: Vertical, galvanized steel straps, 2.5 mm thick, 30 mm wide, with 6 mm holes at 15 mm offset centres and lengths up to 1 m, are fixed over the wall plates and down the face of the inner skin of blockwork at maximum 2 m intervals. Additional straps should be used to reinforce any half-lap wall plate joint. Horizontal straps, 5 mm thick are used across the ceiling joists and rafters, to anchor the gable-end walls.

Ceiling joists: Like floor joists, these should span the shortest distance, rest on and be fixed to the wall plates, as well as to the foot of the rafter on each side – thereby acting as an important tie and also providing a skeleton structure for the boarding of the ceiling. 100 × 50 mm sawn timbers are used.

Common rafters: Again, 100 × 50 mm sawn timber is used for these load-bearing ribs that pitch up from the wall plate on each side of the roof span, to rest opposite each other and be fixed against the ridge board at the top.

Ridge board: The spine of the structure at the apex, running horizontally on edge in the form of a sawn board of about 175 × 32 mm section (deeper on steep roofs), against which the rafters are fixed.

Saddle board: A triangular board (usually of 18 mm plywood) like a gusset plate, fixed at the end of the ridge board and to the face of the first pair of common rafters, to support the hips and crown rafter of a hipped end.

Crown or pin rafter: The central rafter of a hipped end.

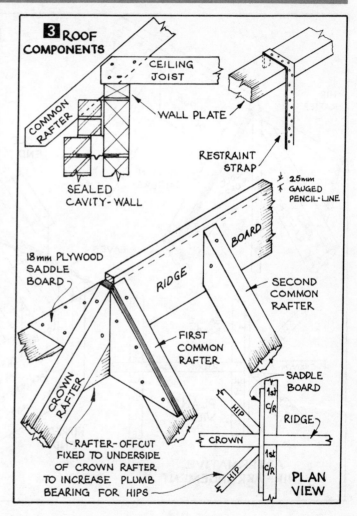

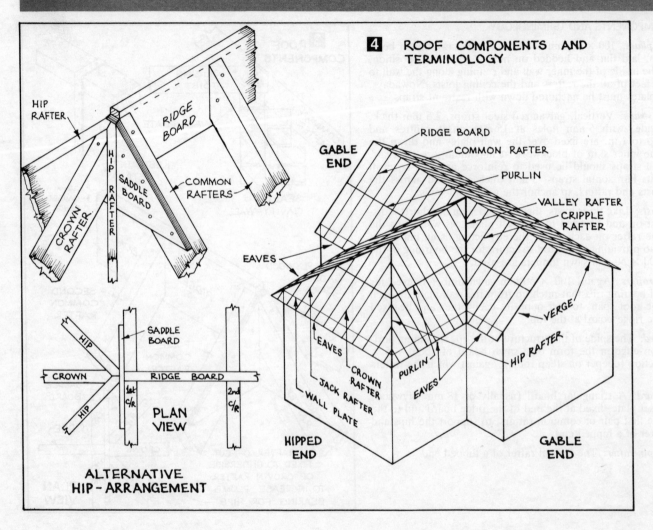

HIP RAFTER

RIDGE BOARD

HIP RAFTER

CROWN RAFTER

SADDLE BOARD

COMMON RAFTERS

4   ROOF COMPONENTS AND TERMINOLOGY

GABLE END

RIDGE BOARD

COMMON RAFTER

PURLIN

VALLEY RAFTER

CRIPPLE RAFTER

EAVES

VERGE

EAVES

CROWN RAFTER

PURLIN

HIP RAFTER

JACK RAFTER

EAVES

WALL PLATE

HIPPED END

GABLE END

SADDLE BOARD

HIP

CROWN   RIDGE BOARD

HIP

1st c/r   2nd c/r

PLAN VIEW

ALTERNATIVE HIP - ARRANGEMENT

5 *Angle tie*: Sometimes a piece of 100 × 50 mm timber, acting as a corner tie across the wall plates, replaces the traditional and elaborate dragon-tie-beam used to counteract the thrust of the hip rafters.

Hip rafters: Similar to ridge boards, but pitching up from the wall-plate corners of a hipped end to the saddle board at the ridge. Acts as a spine for the fixing of the jack rafter heads.

Jack rafters: Rafters with a double splay-cut at the head, fixed in diminishing pairs on each side of the hip rafters.

Valley rafters: Like hip rafters, but forming an internal angle in the roof-formation and acting as a spine for the fixing of the cripple rafters.

Cripple rafters: Pairs of rafters, diminishing like jacks, spanning from ridge boards to valley rafter and gaining their name by being cut off at the foot.

Purlins: Horizontal beams, about 100 to 150 × 75 mm sawn, that support the rafters mid-way between the ridge and wall plate, when the rafters exceed 2.5 m in length.

Struts: 100 × 50 mm sawn timbers that support the purlins at about every fourth or fifth pair of rafters. This arrangement transfers the roof load to the ceiling joists and, therefore, requires a load-bearing wall or partition at right angles to the joists and somewhere near mid-span below.

Straining pieces: Sole plates fixed to the ceiling joists, between the base of the struts, to support and balance the roof thrust.

Collars: These are 100 × 50 mm sawn ties, sometimes used to give extra resistance to roof-spread at purlin level.

Binders: 100 × 50 mm timbers fixed on edge in the roof space with skew-nails or framing anchors at right angles to the ceiling joists, to give support and counteract deflection of joists if the span exceeds 2.5 m.

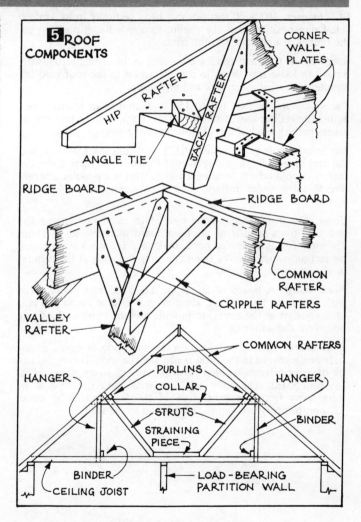

5 ROOF COMPONENTS

6 *Hangers*: 100 × 50 mm ties that hang vertically from a rafter side-fixing position near the purlin, to a side-fixing position on the binder, usually close to the struts.

Roof trap: A trimmed and lined opening in the ceiling joists, with hinged or loose trap door, to provide access to the roof void for maintenance of storage tank and pipes, etc.

Cat walk: One or two 100 to 150 × 25 mm sawn boards fixed across the ceiling joists from the edges of the trap, to provide an access path through the roof (usually to the storage tank).

Lay boards: Sole plates of about 175 × 25 mm sawn section, laid flat and diagonally on a ribbed roof structure, to receive the cut feet of cripple rafters forming a valley. This is a popular alternative to using valley rafters, as it is stronger and involves less work.

Eaves: The lowest edge of the roof which usually overhangs the structure from as little as the facia board thickness up to about 450 mm. This is measured horizontally and is known as an eaves' projection, which may be open (showing the ends of the rafters) or closed on the underside.

Facia board: A board of about ex. 175 × 25 mm p.a.r., fixed with 75 mm or 100 mm cut, clasp or oval nails to the plumb cuts of the rafters at the eaves, to provide a visual finish and a fixing board for the guttering.

Soffit board: Fixed to cradling on the underside of closed eaves, between a groove in the facia board and the wall. This board can be of exterior resin-bonded plywood, asbestos-cement or asbestos fibreboard. The soffit board is sometimes specified to be kept away from the inner face of the facia board by about 12 mm, to provide a gap for ventilation to the roof.

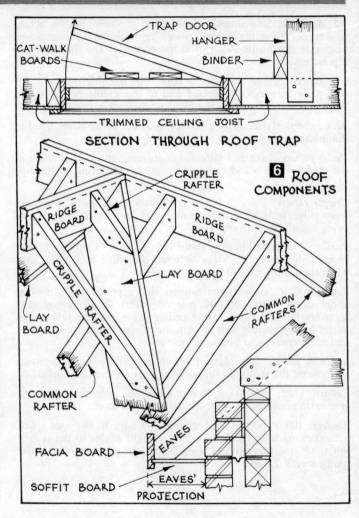

SECTION THROUGH ROOF TRAP

6 ROOF COMPONENTS

7 *Cradling*: Purpose-made L-shaped brackets comprising 50 × 25 mm sawn battens, with simple half-lap corner joints clench-nailed together. The brackets are fixed to the sides of rafters with 63 mm r.h.w. nails to provide soffit-board fixings.

Sprocket pieces: Long wedge-shaped pieces of rafter material, fixed on top of each rafter at the eaves to create a bell-shape appearance or upward tilt to the roof slope. This is also achieved by fixing offcuts of rafter to the rafter sides. Apart from aesthetic reasons, this is done to reduce a steep roof slope, in order to ease the flow of rainwater into the guttering and, in the case of side-fixed sprockets, to alleviate the structural problem of excessive tapering of brickwork below the wall plate.

Tilting fillets: A batten of triangular-shaped cross-section fixed behind the top of a raised facia board to give it support. Tilting fillets are also used in other places, such as on the top edges of valley boards and back-gutters, etc.

Valley boards: 25 mm-thick sawn boards used to form a gutter in the valley, when the valley is to be felted or lined with lead.

Verge: The edge of the roof on a gable end.

Barge boards: Facia boards inclined like a pair of rafters and fixed to the face of the verge on a gable-ended roof. If projecting from the wall, a soffit board may be required, involving a boxed-shape at the eaves on each side.

Tile or slate battens: 38 × 18 mm to 50 × 25 mm sawn battens fixed at gauged spacings on top of the lapped roofing felt. The fixing of these battens is normally done by the slater and tiler, not the carpenter.

Framing anchors: Galvanized steel framing anchors of various shapes may be used to replace traditionally nailed fixings in certain places.

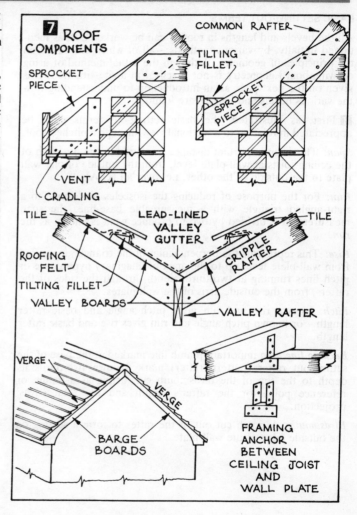

BASIC SETTING-OUT TERMS

All the bevels and lengths in roofing can be worked out, as mentioned initially, by various methods – all of which are based on the principles of geometry. Although the actual method of using drawing-board geometry is not practical in a site situation, it is given on the next page as an introduction to understanding how the various bevels and lengths are found.

8 First, as illustrated, the basic setting-out terms must be appreciated in relation to a sectional view through a pitched roof.

Span: This is an important distance measured in the direction of the ceiling joists at wall-plate level, from the outside of one wall plate to the outside of the other, i.e. over all (O/A).

Run: For the purpose of reducing the isosceles roof shape to a right-angled triangle with a measureable base-line, the span measurement is divided by two to produce what is known as the *run*.

Rise: This represents the perpendicular of the triangle, measured from wall-plate level up to the apex of imaginary hypotenuse or pitch lines running at two-thirds depth through the sides of the rafters, from the outside arris of the wall plates.

Pitch: Known rise and run gives pitch angle and basic rafter length – or known pitch angle and run gives rise and basic rafter length.

Backing line: An important plumb line marked at the base of the setting-out rafter (pattern rafter) marked down two-thirds its depth to the top of the birdsmouth cut, acting as a datum or reference point for the rafter's length and the total eaves' projection.

Birdsmouth: A notch cut out of the rafter to form a seating on the outside edge of the wall plate.

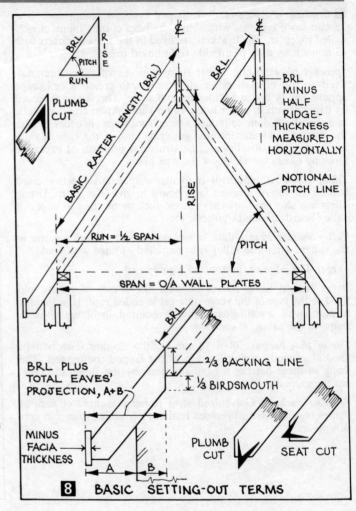

THE GEOMETRICAL SETTING-OUT OF A HIPPED ROOF

9 *Bevels and length of common rafter*: Draw triangle ABC (section through roof). AB = SPAN. AD = RUN (half span). CD = RISE. Angle DAC = SEAT CUT. Angle ACD = PLUMB CUT. Line AC or CB = basic rafter length (BRL).

Bevels and length of hip rafter: Draw plan of roof, showing two hipped ends (always drawn at angles of 45° in equal pitched roofs), shown as A'E, B'E and A"F, B"F. At right angles to B'E, draw line EG, equal in length to RISE at CD. Join G to B'. Angle EB'G is SEAT CUT. Angle B'GE is PLUMB CUT. Line B'G = basic hip rafter length (BHRL).

Hip edge cut: (For square-edged hips.) Draw line HI, parallel to EG at any distance from E, then draw line IJ, equal to distance EH, at right angles to B'I. Draw line JG. Angle JGI is EDGE CUT.

Jack (and cripple) rafter bevels and lengths: With radius CA, describe an arc from A to K, equal to basic rafter length. Project K down to form LM. Join L to E to give elevated, true shape of roof side. Draw single lines to represent rafters at 400 mm (scaled) centres. Angle LEN is Jack/cripple edge cut. (Jack/cripple side cut is the same as Common rafter plumb cut.) Line OP is the basic length of the first jack rafter; QR is the second.

Diminish of jack (and cripple) rafters: The perpendicular, SP, of the triangle RSP, is equal to the constant diminish of the jack (or cripple) rafters.

Purlin bevels: Angle QLR is the purlin edge cut. With compass at D and CB as a tangent at T, describe an arc to cut CD at U. Join U to B. Angle DUB is the purlin side cut.

Dihedral angle or backing bevel: (For top-edge of hips, if required.) Establish triangle A"VF, as at B'GE. Draw a 45° line at any point, marked W'W". With compass at X and A"V as a tangent at Y, describe an arc to cut A"F at Z. Join Z to W' and W". Angle W'ZX or XZW" is the required backing bevel.

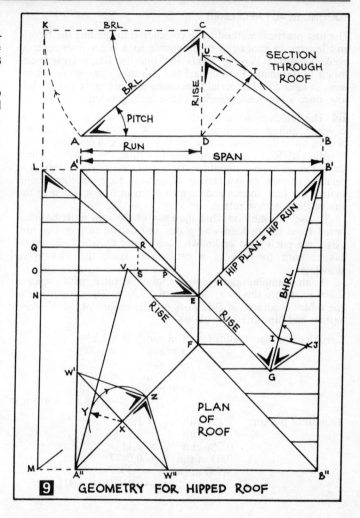

9 GEOMETRY FOR HIPPED ROOF

ROOFING READY RECKONER

The first practical method to be considered for finding the bevels and lengths in roofing is by reference to a small limp-covered booklet entitled *Roofing Ready Reckoner* by Ralph Goss, published by Granada Publishing Ltd. The tables are given separately in metric and imperial dimensions and are quite easy to follow, once a few basic principles have been grasped.

10 The tables cover a variety of roof pitches and the various bevels required and diminish for jack rafters, are given for pitches up to 75°. Basic rafter lengths (BRL) and basic hip rafter lengths (BHRL) must be worked out from the tables – which show a given measurement for the hypotenuse (inclined rafter) in relation to base measurements of metres, decimetres and millimetres (or feet, inches and eighths of an inch) contained in the run of the common rafter.

To use this method, first the span of the roof must be measured from the bedded wall-plates and halved to give the run. Also, the pitch must be known – and if not specified, should be taken, with the aid of a protractor, from the elevational drawings.

As an example, take a hipped roof of 36° pitch, with a span of 7.460 m. Halve this to give a run of 3.730 m. Then, referring to the tables illustrated at **10** , work out the lengths of the common rafters and hip rafters as follows:

Length of common rafter for	1 m run	= 1.236
	3 m run	= 3.708
	0.7 m run	= 0.865
	0.03 m run	= 0.0371
	3.730 m run	= 4.6101
		→ (BRL = 4.610 m)*

Length of hip for:	1 m run	= 1.590
	3 m run	= 4.770
	0.7 m run	= 1.113
	0.03 m run	= 0.0477
	3.730 m run	= 5.9307
		→ (BHRL = 5.931 m)**

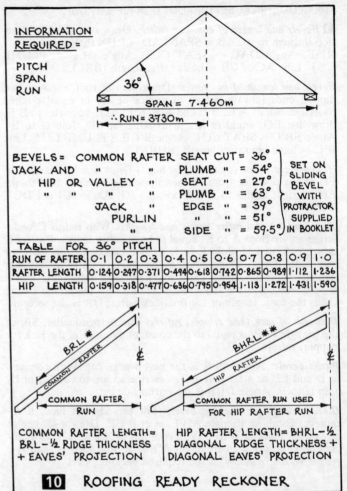

INFORMATION REQUIRED =

PITCH
SPAN
RUN

36°

SPAN = 7.460m

∴ RUN = 3730m

BEVELS =	COMMON RAFTER	SEAT CUT	= 36°	SET ON
JACK AND	" "	PLUMB "	= 54°	SLIDING
HIP OR VALLEY	"	SEAT "	= 27°	BEVEL
" "	" "	PLUMB "	= 63°	WITH
	JACK "	EDGE "	= 39°	PROTRACTOR
	PURLIN	" "	= 51°	SUPPLIED
	"	SIDE "	= 59.5°	IN BOOKLET

TABLE FOR 36° PITCH

RUN OF RAFTER	0·1	0·2	0·3	0·4	0·5	0·6	0·7	0·8	0·9	1·0
RAFTER LENGTH	0·124	0·247	0·371	0·494	0·618	0·742	0·865	0·989	1·112	1·236
HIP LENGTH	0·159	0·318	0·477	0·636	0·795	0·954	1·113	1·272	1·431	1·590

BRL *

COMMON RAFTER

COMMON RAFTER RUN

BHRL **

HIP RAFTER

COMMON RAFTER RUN USED FOR HIP RAFTER RUN

COMMON RAFTER LENGTH = BRL – ½ RIDGE THICKNESS + EAVES' PROJECTION

HIP RAFTER LENGTH = BHRL – ½ DIAGONAL RIDGE THICKNESS + DIAGONAL EAVES' PROJECTION

10   ROOFING READY RECKONER

11 ***Jack rafter diminish:***
All things being equal, jack and cripple rafters should diminish in length by a constant amount in relation to the length of the main rafter (crown or common). The *Ready Reckoner* gives a set of figures for each different pitch, shown on the same page as the bevels and tables, to deal with the decrease according to the spaced centres of the rafters. Assuming rafters to be spaced at 400 mm centres on the 36° pitched roof described on the previous page, then the diminish, as illustrated, would be 494 mm.

12 ***Imperial-dimensioned tables***
As a comparison – and perhaps as an alternative for anyone who has trouble with decimal points used in the basic calculations – the following example is given, using the imperial tables expressed in feet, inches and eighths of an inch. Again, take a hipped roof of 36° pitch, but with a span of 24 ft 5 in. (twenty-four feet, five inches). Halve this to give a run of 12 ft 2½ in. Then, referring to the tables illustrated here, work out the lengths of the common rafters and hip rafters as follows:

Length of common rafter for:	10 ft run	= 12 ft	4⅜ in.
	2 ft run	= 2 ft	5⅜ in.
	2 in. run	=	2½ in.
	½ in. run	=	⅜ in.
	12 ft 2½ in. run	= 15 ft	1⅛ in.
Length of hip rafter for:	10 ft run	= 15 ft	10¾ in.
	2 ft run	= 3 ft	2⅛ in.
	2 in. run	=	3⅛ in.
	½ in. run	=	¾ in.
	12 ft 2½ in. run	= 19 ft	4¾ in.

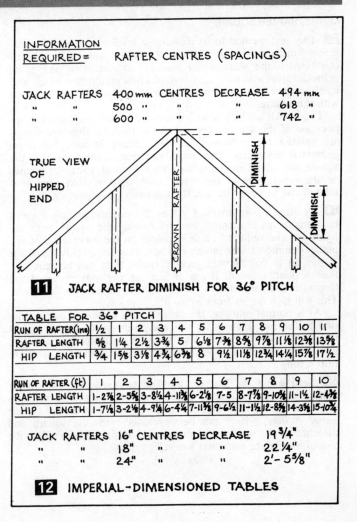

INFORMATION REQUIRED = RAFTER CENTRES (SPACINGS)

JACK RAFTERS 400 mm CENTRES DECREASE 494 mm
" " 500 " " 618 "
" " 600 " " 742 "

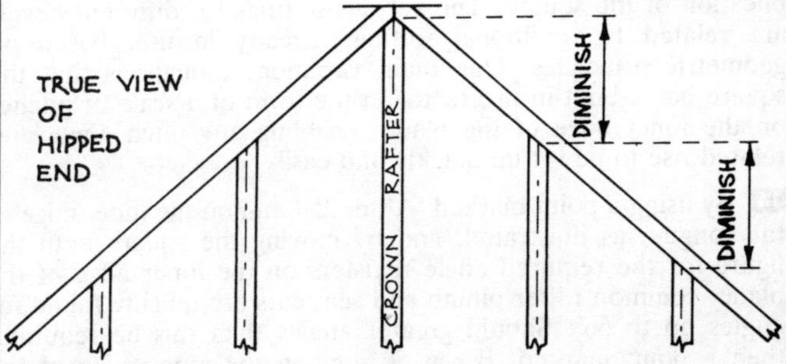

11 JACK RAFTER DIMINISH FOR 36° PITCH

TABLE FOR 36° PITCH

RUN OF RAFTER (ins)	½	1	2	3	4	5	6	7	8	9	10	11
RAFTER LENGTH	⅝	1¼	2½	3¾	5	6⅛	7⅜	8⅝	9⅞	11⅛	12⅜	13⅝
HIP LENGTH	¾	1⅝	3⅛	4¾	6⅜	8	9½	11⅛	12¾	14¼	15⅞	17½

RUN OF RAFTER (ft)	1	2	3	4	5	6	7	8	9	10
RAFTER LENGTH	1-2⅞	2-5⅝	3-8½	4-11⅜	6-2⅛	7-5	8-7⅞	9-10⅝	11-1½	12-4⅜
HIP LENGTH	1-7⅛	3-2⅛	4-9¼	6-4¼	7-11⅜	9-6½	11-1½	12-8⅝	14-3⅝	15-10¾

JACK RAFTERS 16" CENTRES DECREASE 19¾"
" " 18" " " 22¼"
" " 24" " " 2'-5⅝"

12 IMPERIAL-DIMENSIONED TABLES

METRIC RAFTER SQUARE

13 The next method to be considered involves the use of a traditional instrument known as a *steel roofing square* or its modern counterpart, the *metric rafter square* – so named by one of its manufacturers who have also devised a new method for its use and have produced an explanatory booklet on the subject, available with the square.

The booklet, which is well illustrated, clearly explains the application of the square. The various settings for different bevels are related to traditional settings already in use, based on geometric principles. One main variation, though, is that the square has a built-in protractor in the form of a scale of pitches on the inner edge of the blade, enabling any pitch angle and related rise to be set up quickly and easily.

14 By using a point marked 'A', at 250 mm on the inner edge of the tongue, as illustrated, and by moving the square until the figure for the required angle registers on the inner edge of the blade, common rafter plumb and seat cuts are quickly found for angles up to 66°. Should greater angles than this be required, then a point marked 'B', at 50 mm on the inner edge of the tongue is used in relation to the scale of pitches on the blade. This will give angles from 66° to 85°.

As is normal practice, the rafter length is worked out in relation to the run. Figures for this are given on the blade, against the pitch, related to a 1 m run. Hence, a small calculation will be necessary, according to how many metres or parts of a metre are in the run.

15 Setting out the first common rafter, used as a pattern for setting out all the others, is the next operation, illustrated as shown in the booklet. This can be greatly aided by the use of *stair gauge fittings*, which can be purchased with the square and attached to the square's edges to act as stops – thus avoiding the use of a separate carpenter's bevel.

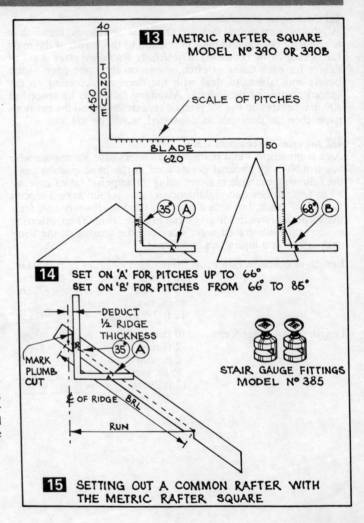

13 METRIC RAFTER SQUARE
MODEL N° 390 OR 390B

SCALE OF PITCHES

TONGUE
450
40

BLADE
620
50

35° A   68° B

14 SET ON 'A' FOR PITCHES UP TO 66°
SET ON 'B' FOR PITCHES FROM 66° TO 85°

DEDUCT ½ RIDGE THICKNESS

35° A

MARK PLUMB CUT

℄ OF RIDGE   RL

RUN

STAIR GAUGE FITTINGS
MODEL N° 385

15 SETTING OUT A COMMON RAFTER WITH THE METRIC RAFTER SQUARE

STEEL ROOFING SQUARE

16 There are at least four variations on the use of the traditional steel square. These variations apply to methods for finding the lengths of the rafters and not to formulas for finding the various bevels. The bevels – or *cuts*, as they are referred to in roofing terminology – relate to basic principles of geometry with only one definition. Visualizing the geometrical definitions, by imagining the roofing square being held against or within a scaled-down roof structure, as illustrated, is a good way to remember the different formulas.

The various methods for finding the main rafter lengths are:
1. The scaled method.
2. The foot run and pitch method.
3. By calculations in trigonometry.
4. The foot run and rise method. This is related to tables printed on the body of the square, which involve calculations to find the rise in inches per foot run, the length of the rafter per foot run and a separate working out for the additional length of rafter per odd inches of run.

17 The first two methods, being preferred for their simplicity, are given here. Also preferred, are American pattern stair gauge fittings, illustrated separately and on the sides of the square.

Scaled method
This is first used to find the common rafter length, plumb cut and seat cut:

18 If using an imperial-dimensioned square, the scale used will be one-twelfth full size, whereby the inches on the square represent feet and the twelfths-of-an-inch represent inches. As illustrated, a run of, say, 10 ft 2 in. is set on the blade at 10 $\frac{2}{12}$ in., in relation to a rise of, say, 6 ft 6 in. being set on the tongue at 6$\frac{6}{12}$ in. (6½ in.). These settings determine the plumb and seat cuts and provide a scaled measurement of the rafter length. If using a metric square, the scale will be one-tenth full size and is easily achieved by moving the decimal point, i.e. 3.100 m run ÷ 10 = 0.310 mm and 1.980 m rise ÷ 10 = 0.198 mm.

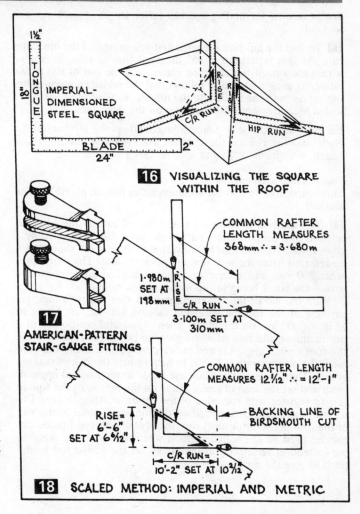

16 VISUALIZING THE SQUARE WITHIN THE ROOF

17 AMERICAN-PATTERN STAIR-GAUGE FITTINGS

18 SCALED METHOD: IMPERIAL AND METRIC

Scaled method for finding the hip rafter length, plumb cut and seat cut:

19 To find the hip rafter length, first you must find the hip rafter run. As this represents a 45° diagonal line in plan, contained within the run of the common rafter, and the run of the crown rafter, forming a square, it follows that the scaled common-rafter run set on both the blade and the tongue, as illustrated, gives the scaled measurement of the hip run on the diagonal.

20 Now alter the stair gauge fittings and set the hip run on the blade and the rise on the tongue. This will give the hip rafter length, plumb cut (P/C) and seat cut (S/C).

Foot run and pitch method
This is first used to find the common rafter length, plumb cut and seat cut.

21 This method only uses 1 ft (12 in.) of run on the blade in relation to a proportionate part of the total rise, controlled by a given pitch. This can also be converted to metric, but should then be referred to as the *unit run and pitch method*. The *unit* represents 300 mm and metric or imperial-marked squares can be used – the latter being set up with a metric rule.

With the aid of the American pattern stair gauge fittings, regardless of the run measurement, always set the first fitting at 12 in. or 300 mm on the blade. Then, by careful positioning of a protractor on the face of a straightedge board (or rafter), mark the roof's pitch angle (a) and indicate which side is the required pitch (b), as illustrated. This is to help reduce the risk of making errors. Then, line up the 12 on the blade to the marked angle of pitch and set the second gauge fitting on the tongue of the square (c), to register with the edge of the rafter or straightedge. The measurement now determined on the tongue is equal to the rise of the roof per foot (or unit) run. Incidentally, this technique can also be used on the scaled method when the rise is not known, but instead of setting 12 on the blade, set the scaled run to the pitch to give the total rise.

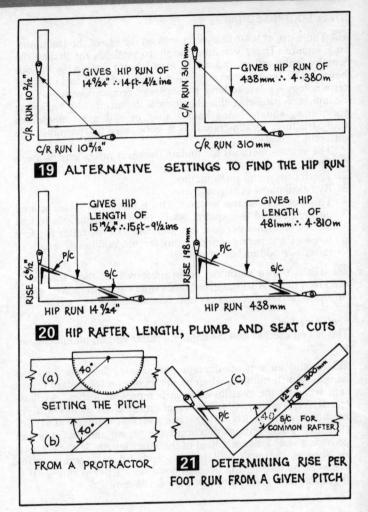

19 ALTERNATIVE SETTINGS TO FIND THE HIP RUN

— GIVES HIP RUN OF 14 9/24" ∴ 14 ft - 4½ ins
— GIVES HIP RUN OF 438mm ∴ 4·380m
C/R RUN 10 2/12"
C/R RUN 310 mm

20 HIP RAFTER LENGTH, PLUMB AND SEAT CUTS

— GIVES HIP LENGTH OF 15 19/24" ∴ 15ft - 9½ ins
— GIVES HIP LENGTH OF 481mm ∴ 4·810m
RISE 6 6/12" HIP RUN 14 9/24" P/C S/C
RISE 198 mm HIP RUN 438mm P/C S/C

(a) 40° SETTING THE PITCH
(b) 40° FROM A PROTRACTOR

(c) 12" or 300mm P/C 40° S/C FOR COMMON RAFTER

21 DETERMINING RISE PER FOOT RUN FROM A GIVEN PITCH

Foot run and pitch method for finding the hip rafter length, plumb cut and seat cut:

22 The rise per foot run, determined by protractor for the common rafter, is now set on the tongue again, in relation to 17 in. on the blade. 17 in., (16.97 in. actually) as illustrated, is the diagonal of 12 in. squared. In other words, for every 12 in. of common rafter run, the hip run is 17 in. In metric, 424 mm is the diagonal of 300 mm squared.

Setting out a common rafter

23 This should be double-checked, as this first rafter acts as a pattern for marking out the rest. When cut, only one rafter should be marked and cut from it, the pair laid on the ground with an offcut of ridge board between the plumb cuts and a tape measure stretched across the birdsmouth cuts to check the span. If satisfactory, the rest of the commons may be cut, keeping any cambered or 'sprung' edges on top.

24 First, mark a seat (a) and plumb cut (b) for the facia and soffit boards. Check the concealed and visible eaves' projection on the drawing and set this in to a plumb cut representing the backing line (c). Check the depth of this line, divide it by three and mark down two-thirds to the birdsmouth seat cut (d). These cuts are marked with the square held in the appropriate positions, as illustrated.

25 Next, mark the rafter length. If by scaled method, the scaled-up measurement can be run on the back of the rafter, from the top of the backing line to the top of a plumb cut equal to the centre of the ridge board. Slide the square down and mark the final plumb cut at half the ridge board thickness, measured horizontally. If using the foot or unit run method, the square can be stepped up the rafter – care being taken not to build up cumulative errors via a blunt pencil or faulty stepping – or the hypotenuse measurement on the square may be multiplied by the number of feet or units in the run, to result in one measurement as before. Any fractions of a foot or unit are dealt with as shown.

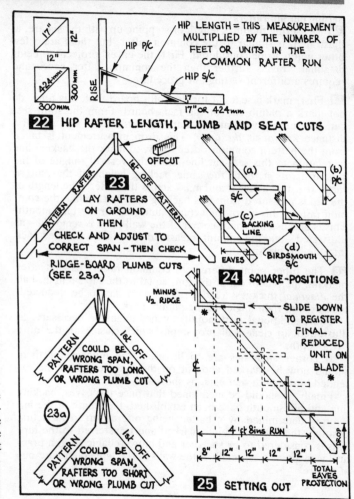

Setting out hip rafters

26 Measuring the hip's length or stepping up with the square, as illustrated, is similar to the common rafter, but there are a few other points to be considered. First, the eaves' projection, being diagonal, travels further than the common rafter eaves and requires a different setting-out procedure.

27 First, mark a seat cut for the soffit board, but, this time, do not mark a plumb cut for the facia board. From the soffit seat cut, measure up vertically to mark the birdsmouth seat cut, at a distance known as *the drop*. This drop measurement is taken from the pattern common rafter. Now, to mark the backing line in relation to this seat-cut line, slide the vertical tongue of the square across it, until the same backing height of the pattern rafter registers above it and mark across the rafter. The length of the hip is measured from this backing line, but, unlike the common rafters, this is not the actual plumb cut for the birdsmouth. This is because the sharp corner of the wall plate is removed – as illustrated – and the amount, measured diagonally, is added back into the hip birdsmouth.

28 The other point different to common rafters, is that after marking the plumb cut at the top, equal to the hip's length, half the *diagonal* thickness of the ridge board has to be deducted, measured at right angles to the plumb mark.

Also, additional birdsmouth notches might be necessary, as illustrated, to clear wall projections which clash with the hip's extra depth.

If corner angle-ties are to be used, the notches for them should now be marked and cut on the inner edges of the extended birdsmouth seat cuts, as shown at **27**.

Finally, it should be mentioned that once the eaves, backing line and birdsmouth have been established, the length of the hip is often determined by a batten being offered up to its actual position, the extreme points marked and transferred to the hip. This is considered to be speedier and more reliable from a practical view point – especially if the walls at the hipped end are out of square.

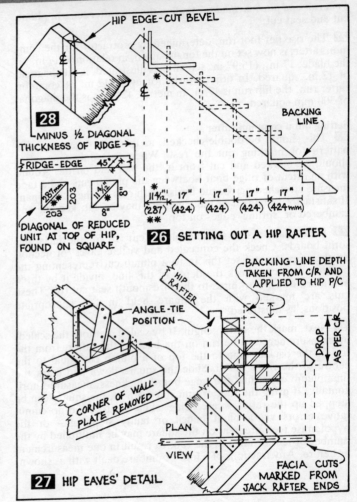

HIP EDGE-CUT BEVEL

28 MINUS ½ DIAGONAL THICKNESS OF RIDGE

RIDGE-EDGE 45°

287mm / 203   11½" / 8"

DIAGONAL OF REDUCED UNIT AT TOP OF HIP, FOUND ON SQUARE

BACKING LINE

11½" (287) 17" (424) 17" (424) 17" (424) 17" (424mm)

26 SETTING OUT A HIP RAFTER

BACKING-LINE DEPTH TAKEN FROM C/R AND APPLIED TO HIP P/C

HIP RAFTER

ANGLE-TIE POSITION

CORNER OF WALL-PLATE REMOVED

DROP AS PER C/R

PLAN VIEW

FACIA CUTS MARKED FROM JACK RAFTER ENDS

27 HIP EAVES' DETAIL

Hip edge cut

29 This is applied to the edges of the hip plumb cut and enables the hips to fit into the heads of the crown rafter and the first common rafters, against a saddle board – or, alternatively, to fit against each other and the saddle board. A simpler way of finding the edge bevel, is to measure and mark half the hip's thickness (x) in from the plumb cut each side. This gives the three points for marking the edge bevels, as illustrated.

Hip backing bevel (*dihedral angle*)

30 This is used when the roof is to be boarded and is applied by planing from both sides to a top centre line. Mostly obsolete nowadays.

Jack side cut

This is the same formula as for the common rafter plumb cut, with scaled run (or a unit of run) on the blade and rise on the tongue, related to pitch. The cut is marked on the tongue.

Jack edge cut

31 (a) This combines with the above cut to make a compound angle to fit against the hip or valley rafters.

Purlin edge cut

(b) This is applied to the surface that the rafters rest on, to form a mitred top edge against the sides and under the centre of the hip or valley rafters.

Purlin side cut

32 This combines with the above cut, to complete the mitred faces against and under the hips or valley rafters.

Purlin lip cut

33 As illustrated, this is simply marked at 90° to the purlin side cut in relation to the amount of hip projection below the rafters.

Jack rafter diminish

34 By setting the jack edge-cut formula on the square, this can easily be found on the blade, as illustrated.

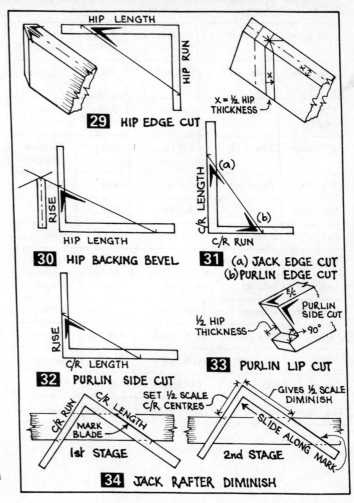

29 HIP EDGE CUT

30 HIP BACKING BEVEL

31 (a) JACK EDGE CUT (b) PURLIN EDGE CUT

32 PURLIN SIDE CUT

33 PURLIN LIP CUT

34 JACK RAFTER DIMINISH

Table of bevel formulas (for quick reference)

Component	Required bevel	Blade setting	Tongue setting	Side for marking
Common rafter	Plumb cut	C/R run	Rise	Tongue
Common rafter	Seat cut	C/R run	Rise	Blade
Hip rafter	Run of hip	C/R run	C/R run	Diagonal distance
Hip rafter	Plumb cut	Hip run	Rise	Tongue
Hip rafter	Seat cut	Hip run	Rise	Blade
Hip rafter	Edge cut	Hip length	Hip run	Blade
Hip rafter	Backing bevel	Hip length	Rise	Tongue
Jack rafter	Side cut	C/R run	Rise	Tongue
Jack rafter	Edge cut	C/R length	C/R run	Blade
Purlin	Edge cut	C/R length	C/R run	Tongue
Purlin	Side cut	C/R length	Rise	Tongue
Lay board	Plumb cut	C/R length	C/R run	Blade
Lay board	Seat cut	C/R length	C/R run	Tongue

Templates

35 As the various bevels are determined on a roof job, they are usually marked onto the face of a spare piece of p.a.r. boarding for easy reference and are identified with abbreviations such as Jack Edge Cut (Jack E/C), etc. From this, they may be reset, when required, onto the steel square by use of the stair gauge fittings, or they may be transferred to a carpenter's sliding bevel; alternatively, small templates with wooden fences may be made up to the required angles, as illustrated. Note that the fences are kept in to allow a quick, uninhibited stroke of the pencil across the bevelled edge.

PITCHING DETAILS AND SEQUENCE

Bedding the wall plates is best done as a joint effort between carpenter and bricklayer. The bricklayer spreads the mortar, beds and levels the plates and the carpenter checks that they are square (3 : 4 : 5 method) and parallel to each other across the span. To achieve this, slight lateral adjustments of the plates may be made – within reason.

Gable roof

36 When the plates are set, the ridge board may be laid against the wall plate, if possible, and the positions of the common rafters spaced out and marked across both members. Next, the vertical restraint straps are fixed over the plates – and the joists, with any sprung edges kept uppermost, are fixed adjacent to the rafter marks, either by skew-nailing with 75 or 100 mm r.h.w. nails or by being fixed into shoe-type framing anchors. The joists, also fixed to the plates of any internal cross-walls, act as a working platform and should be close or open-boarded with an area of scaffold boards.

37 At each end of the roof, a pair of rafters is pitched and fixed to the wall plates *and* the joists, their plumb cuts supporting each other at the apex. This is a two-man job. An interlocking scaffold can be erected through the ceiling-joist area and, from this, the ridge board is pushed up between the rafter plumb-cuts and fixed into position. On each fixing, one 75 mm r.h.w. nail is driven through the top edge of the rafter and two – one on each side – are skew-nailed through the sides into the ridge board.

According to the length of the roof and whether the purlins or ridge board are to be jointed, a few more pairs of rafters may be fixed at strategic positions, then the purlins are offered up and fixed by skew-nailing from above. The struts are fixed, then – to

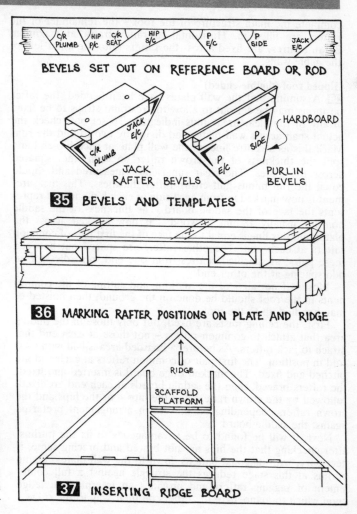

BEVELS SET OUT ON REFERENCE BOARD OR ROD

JACK RAFTER BEVELS

PURLIN BEVELS

HARDBOARD

35 BEVELS AND TEMPLATES

36 MARKING RAFTER POSITIONS ON PLATE AND RIDGE

RIDGE

SCAFFOLD PLATFORM

37 INSERTING RIDGE BOARD

complete the main structure of the roof – the remainder of the rafters are filled in. Horizontal restraint straps, at maximum 2.0 m centres, are fixed across the rafters onto the inner leaf of the gable walls.

Hipped roof (double-ended)

38 Assuming that the wall plates have been bedded, the rafter positions may be set out to allow the restraint straps to be fixed in any of the clear areas thus indicated. To set out, check the actual span across wall plates and divide by two to find the run. Mark this as a centre line on the wall plate at each hip-end and split the thickness of the crown rafter on each side, squared across the plates. The clear run is now measured and should equal the run minus half crown-rafter thickness. This measurement is now marked in from each side of each hip-end and represents the face of the saddle board. The thickness of the saddle board – usually 18 mm plywood – is now marked across the plates and this line is equal to the face of the first pair of common rafters at each end. The other rafters are spaced out between these pairs, at specified centres from one end, regardless of an odd spacing at the other end.

Most – if not all – of the marking and cutting of the components in the roof should be done on the ground, then hoisted or man-handled up to the roof.

First, the ceiling joists are fixed, but only those in the middle area that attach to common rafters – not those at each end that attach to jack rafters. As before, a boarded area is laid with scaffold in position. The first pair of common rafters at each end are pitched and fixed. The marked ridge board is inserted and fixed, the rafters braced, then the saddle boards at each end are fixed, followed by the crown rafters and the hips – or the hips and the crown rafters, depending on the crown arrangement preferred against the saddle board.

Next, it will be found to be advantageous to fix the purlins, after checking that the hips are not bowed and bracing same, if necessary, with diagonal battens down to the wall plates. Fixing purlins at this stage reduces the struggle against a full complement of sagging rafters and provides an intermediate ledge upon which to manoeuvre the rafters on their way to the ridge.

39 Finally, fix jack rafters, remaining joists, binders and struts, etc. then remaining rafters to complete the main structure of the roof. On hipped roofs, short return joists are fixed to the feet of the crown and jack rafters at the hipped ends, as illustrated.

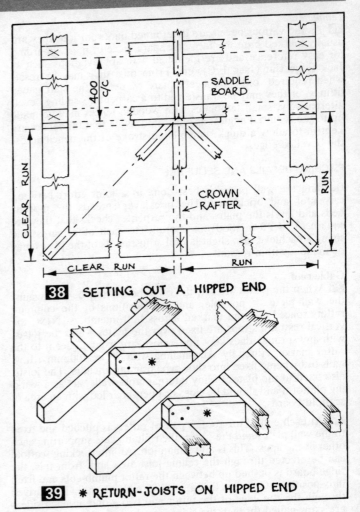

38 SETTING OUT A HIPPED END

39 * RETURN-JOISTS ON HIPPED END

DORMER WINDOWS AND SKYLIGHTS

Roof lights in the form of dormer windows and skylights are usually found in roof spaces used for storage or habitation. Both of these windows involve a trimmed opening in the roof slope and the use of thicker trimming and trimmer rafters, according to size and the amount of trimmed rafters to be carried. The trimming rafters can also be formed by fixing two common rafters together, as illustrated.

Dormer windows

40 These protrude vertically from the eaves or middle area of the roof and have triangular sides known as cheeks, framed up from 100 × 50 mm studs. The windows are usually casement or pivot type and the studded cheeks should be filled with insulation – as per Part F of the Building Regulations – lined internally with foiled gypsum plasterboard and sheathed externally with ex. 25 mm diagonal boarding or 20 mm plywood and may be felted, slated or tiled, etc. onto a background of building paper. The roof may be flat and the 100 × 50 mm joists firred to slope backwards or to fall to a front gutter and corner downpipe which discharges onto the main roof. The modern covering for this roof would be Nuralite or three-layer built-up felt with chippings.

Dormer roofs may also be pitched with a gablet end or hipped end and tiled or slated in keeping with the main roof. Whatever the roof, the ceiling area should, of course, be insulated. Typical construction details are seen in the illustration.

Skylights

These lay in the same plane as the roof slope and traditionally consisted of a glazed skylight window, hinged on the underside at the top and fixed to a raised curb or lining. Although lead or zinc aprons were often fixed to the back and side edges of the skylight, these windows were not always weathertight.

41 Modern skylights, referred to as roof windows by the manufacturers, are a different proposition. These skylights are very sophisticated and reliable. They are made from preservative-impregnated Swedish pine, clad on the exterior with aluminium. The sashes are of the horizontal pivot type with patent locks, seals and draught excluders, and are double glazed with sealed units. The windows, suitable for roof pitches between 20° and 85°, are easily fixed to the rafters with metal L-shaped ties. Metal flashings are supplied with each unit.

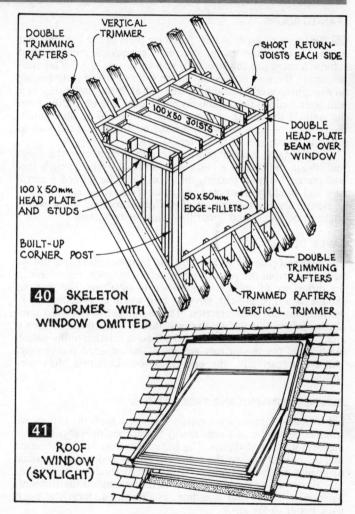

40 SKELETON DORMER WITH WINDOW OMITTED

DOUBLE TRIMMING RAFTERS
VERTICAL TRIMMER
SHORT RETURN JOISTS EACH SIDE
100 × 50 JOISTS
DOUBLE HEAD-PLATE BEAM OVER WINDOW
100 × 50 mm HEAD PLATE AND STUDS
50 × 50 mm EDGE-FILLETS
BUILT-UP CORNER POST
DOUBLE TRIMMING RAFTERS
TRIMMED RAFTERS
VERTICAL TRIMMER

41 ROOF WINDOW (SKYLIGHT)

LEAN-TO ROOFS

42 This type of roof, usually found on parts of the building that extend beyond the main structure, comprises mono-pitched rafters 'leaning' on the structural wall in various ways. This connection to the wall was usually in the form of a wall plate resting on wrought-iron corbels built into the wall at about 1 m centres, or a wall plate bedded on continuous brick corbelling projecting from the wall. If the thrust of a particular roof could be discounted, the connection may be simply a ridge board fixed to the wall to take the plumb cuts of the rafters.

Traditionally, ceiling joists were either built into the main wall, or, in the case of a party wall, notched over iron-corbelled wall plates. Without purlins, this roof would be termed a *single roof* and would be restricted to a span of about 2.4 m.

Before leaving the subject of traditional roofing, a few points ought to be mentioned about the following two items.

EAVES' DETAILS

The seat and plumb cuts for soffit and facia boards should always be marked from the pattern rafter before erection, regardless of the difference of opinion about when to cut them. The seat cut should always be pre-cut, anyway, as it would be extremely awkward to cut this after erection. The plumb cut is often left until all the rafters – including the jack rafters – are pitched, then a chalk line is snapped over the top edges, in relation to the plumb marks, and the in-situ cuts are made and adjusted accordingly. Unless cut carefully, the end result can be worse than pre-cutting.

CHIMNEY-TRIMMING AND BACK GUTTERS

43 When a chimney stack passes through a roof, the rafters are trimmed around it in a similar way to trimmed openings for dormer windows or skylights. The trimmer rafters are stop-housed or butt-jointed against the trimming rafters and may be vertical or leaning to the roof pitch. The former method is preferred, as this allows the trimmed rafters a better bearing on the trimmer. Triangular blocks and boarding, as illustrated, form the usual back gutter to the stack.

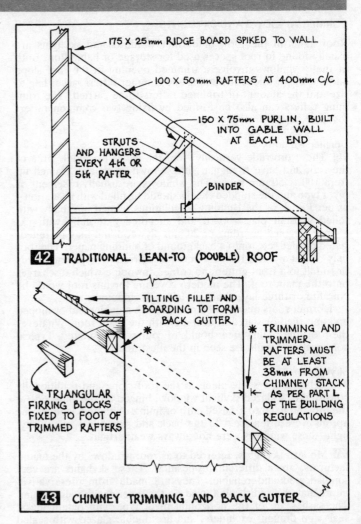

42 TRADITIONAL LEAN-TO (DOUBLE) ROOF

- 175 × 25 mm RIDGE BOARD SPIKED TO WALL
- 100 × 50 mm RAFTERS AT 400 mm C/C
- 150 × 75 mm PURLIN, BUILT INTO GABLE WALL AT EACH END
- STRUTS AND HANGERS EVERY 4th OR 5th RAFTER
- BINDER

43 CHIMNEY TRIMMING AND BACK GUTTER

- TILTING FILLET AND BOARDING TO FORM BACK GUTTER
- TRIANGULAR FIRRING BLOCKS FIXED TO FOOT OF TRIMMED RAFTERS
- ∗ TRIMMING AND TRIMMER RAFTERS MUST BE AT LEAST 38 mm FROM CHIMNEY STACK AS PER PART L OF THE BUILDING REGULATIONS

TRUSSED RAFTERS

44 As mentioned briefly in the opening paragraphs of this chapter, roofing on domestic dwellings is now predominantly comprised of factory-made units in the form of triangulated frames referred to as trussed rafters. These assemblies are made from stress-graded, p.a.r. timber, to a wide variety of configurations according to requirements. Each shape has a name given to it for reference and the two most common designs used in domestic roofing are the 'Fink' or 'W' truss and the 'Fan' truss. All joints are butt-jointed and sandwiched within face-fixing plates on each side. These plates are usually of galvanized steel with closely-spaced holes for nailing or, more commonly, integral, punched-out spikes for factory-pressing – but may also be gang-nailed gusset plates of 12 mm thick resin-bonded plywood. After erection, the trusses should be permanently braced.

The bracing arrangement, details and illustrations given here on trussed-rafter roofs, are based on illustrated information given in the technical manuals obtained from one of the leading manufacturers of these components.

One of the main advantages of this type of roof is the clear span achieved, without the need for load-bearing partitions; standard trusses are available up to 11 m span, with pitches up to 35°. Beyond this span, the manufacturer's design department should be consulted.

It is important to realize that although the trusses are strong enough to resist the eventual load of the roofing materials, they are not strong enough to resist certain pressures applied by severe lateral bending. These pressures can have a de-laminating effect on the plated joints and are most likely to occur during truss delivery, movement across the site, site storage and lifting into position – especially see-sawing over the top edges of walls when the truss is laying on its side face.

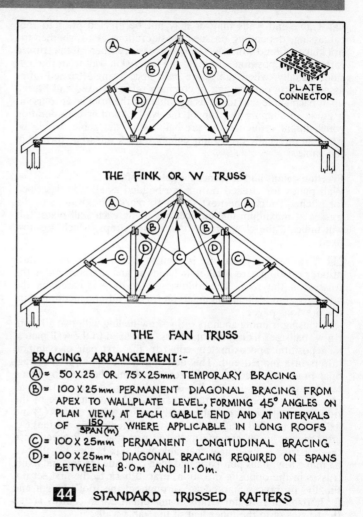

THE FINK OR W TRUSS

PLATE CONNECTOR

THE FAN TRUSS

BRACING ARRANGEMENT :-

Ⓐ = 50 X 25 OR 75 X 25mm TEMPORARY BRACING

Ⓑ = 100 X 25mm PERMANENT DIAGONAL BRACING FROM APEX TO WALLPLATE LEVEL, FORMING 45° ANGLES ON PLAN VIEW, AT EACH GABLE END AND AT INTERVALS OF $\frac{150}{\text{SPAN(m)}}$ WHERE APPLICABLE IN LONG ROOFS

Ⓒ = 100 X 25mm PERMANENT LONGITUDINAL BRACING

Ⓓ = 100 X 25mm DIAGONAL BRACING REQUIRED ON SPANS BETWEEN 8·0m AND 11·0m.

44 STANDARD TRUSSED RAFTERS

45 Gable-end walls may or may not be erected prior to roof carcassing, depending on such considerations as to whether the bricklayer should work *overhand* – necessary when all the trussed rafters are in position – to build the inner-skin wall from the outside. Usually, when gables are built first, a single trussed-rafter assembly or a pattern pair of common rafters is fixed and braced up at each gable end to act as a profile for the bricklayer to use as a guide in shaping the top of the wall. Another consideration which might influence the pre-building of the gable, would be when an internally-protruding chimney stack was to be formed in the gable.

Erection details and sequence for gable roofs:
Wall plates for trussed rafters are bedded as already described for pitched roofs. The next step is to mark the positions of the trusses at maximum 600 mm centres along each wall plate; this will indicate the clear areas for restraint straps, which are now fixed.

46 The erection procedure is open to a certain amount of variation, providing care is taken in handling and pre-positioning the trusses on the roof. The following procedure is based on the notes given in technical manuals on trussed rafters, mentioned on the previous page.

By using framing anchors or by skew-nailing with two 100 mm r.h.w. nails per fixing, the first truss ① is fixed to the wall plates, in a position approximately equal to the first pair of common rafters in a hipped end. This determines the apex for the diagonal braces marked Ⓑ Stabilize and plumb the truss by fixing temporary raking braces Ⓔ on each side, down to the wall plates. Fix temporary battens, marked Ⓐ, on each side of the ridge and resting on the gable wall. Position the next truss ② and fix to the marked wall plate and to the temporary battens Ⓐ, after measuring or gauging to the correct spacing. Proceed until the last truss is fixed near the gable wall. Fix braces Ⓑ with two 63 mm r.h.w. nails per fixing and then continue placing and fixing trusses in the opposite direction, braced back to the first set up. Finally, fix braces marked Ⓒ throughout the roof's length and fix horizontal restraint straps at maximum 2.0 m centres across the trusses onto the inner leaf of the gable walls.

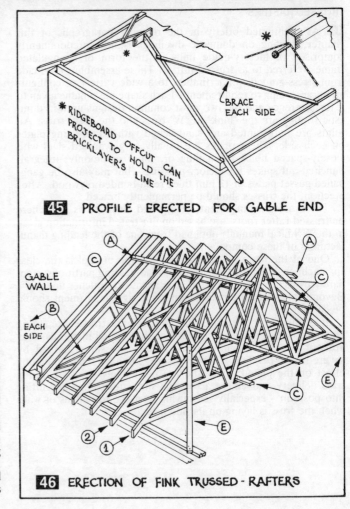

45 PROFILE ERECTED FOR GABLE END

* RIDGEBOARD OFFCUT CAN PROJECT TO HOLD THE BRICKLAYER'S LINE

BRACE EACH SIDE

46 ERECTION OF FINK TRUSSED-RAFTERS

GABLE WALL

EACH SIDE

Hipped roofs under 6.0 m span

47 As illustrated, the recommended hip-end for a roof of this span is of traditional construction. The main difference being that instead of the saddle board and hips being fixed to a ridge board and the first pair of common rafters, they are fixed onto a *girder of standard trussed rafters*. This consists of three standard trussed rafters securely nailed together – on site – through all members at 400 mm centres.

After the wall plates are bedded, the hipped ends are set out as already described for traditional roofing, the positions of the standard trusses marked – and the vertical restraint straps fixed. The erection sequence starts with the fixing and bracing of the girder trusses, followed by the infil of the standard trusses and permanent bracing. The hip ends are then constructed, using hips and rafters at least 25 mm deeper than the truss rafters, to allow for birdsmouthing to the wall plates.

Hipped roofs over 6.0 m span

48 Although the hip end for a roof with a greater span looks complicated when drawn, it is relatively simple to construct. Three special trusses, known as *hip girder trusses*, are again nailed together on site as described above. The girder is fixed at the half-span (run) position and infil ceiling joists are laid and fixed. In three positions, as illustrated, other special trusses rest across the ceiling joists and are fixed to them and to the vertical members of the girder truss. These secondary trusses are known as *hip mono trusses* and six are required at each hip end. Two in the centre are blocked out and fixed to straddle the girder member and house a half-length crown rafter. The other trusses, nailed together in pairs, are fixed on each side of the girder truss and are jointed to the hip rafters. A short purlin and vertical struts are fixed to the mono trusses. Hips and jack rafters, as before, must be at least 25 mm deeper to allow for birdsmouthing to the purlin and wall plates.

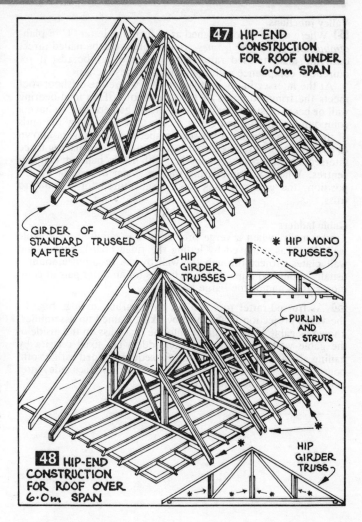

47 HIP-END CONSTRUCTION FOR ROOF UNDER 6.0m SPAN

GIRDER OF STANDARD TRUSSED RAFTERS

HIP GIRDER TRUSSES

* HIP MONO TRUSSES

PURLIN AND STRUTS

48 HIP-END CONSTRUCTION FOR ROOF OVER 6.0m SPAN

HIP GIRDER TRUSS

Valley junctions

49 Where a roof is so designed as to form the letter 'T' in plan, *diminishing jack rafter frames*, as illustrated, can be nailed direct onto the main trussed rafters in relation to lay boards, if required, in compliance with manufacturer's instructions.

At the intersecting point marked Ⓐ, where the offshoot roof meets the trimmed eaves of the main roof – if no load-bearing wall or beam exists at this position – it will be necessary to have a compound of *intersection girder trusses*. This is to carry the ends of the trimmed standard trusses via special joist hangers known as *girder truss shoes*. The girder is formed on site by nailing three intersection-girder-trusses together with r.h.w nails at 400 mm centres. Where a load-bearing wall or beam does exist at this position, the girder trusses can be substituted for a standard truss.

Gable ladders

Traditionally, when a verge projection was required on a gable wall, this was achieved by letting the ridge board, purlins and wall plates project through the wall by the required amount – usually about 200 mm – to act as fixings for an outer pair of common rafters and/or the barge boards.

50 As trussed-rafter roofs do not have purlins or ridge boards, the verge-projection is achieved by fixing framed-up assemblies, known as gable ladders, direct onto the first truss on the inside of the gable wall, as illustrated. The ladders are fixed on site by nailing at 400 mm centres and are subsequently lined with a soffit board on the underside and barge boards on the face side, after being built-in by the bricklayer.

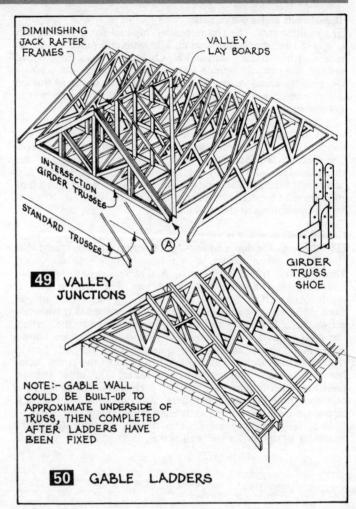

DIMINISHING JACK RAFTER FRAMES

VALLEY LAY BOARDS

INTERSECTION GIRDER TRUSSES

STANDARD TRUSSES

Ⓐ

49 VALLEY JUNCTIONS

GIRDER TRUSS SHOE

NOTE:– GABLE WALL COULD BE BUILT-UP TO APPROXIMATE UNDERSIDE OF TRUSS, THEN COMPLETED AFTER LADDERS HAVE BEEN FIXED

50 GABLE LADDERS

Roof trap

When trusses are spaced at 600 mm centres, it should be possible to simply fix trimmer noggings between the bottom chords of the trusses to form the required roof-trap hatch. In other cases, when the trusses are closer together or a bigger hatch is required, it may be necessary to cut the bottom chord of one of the trusses, as illustrated.

51 Typical details are shown for forming a trap hatch in the central bay of the trussed rafters. First, ex. 38 mm thick framing members are fixed to the inside faces of the ceiling joists that will be acting as trimming joists. Then, two 150 × 38 mm boards, spanning three trusses, must be fixed in position on each side of the hatch before the central ceiling-joist chord is cut. The boards are fixed on the underside to the side of the ceiling-joist ties with framing anchors and 31 mm × 9 gauge square twisted sherardized nails, as per manufacturer's instructions. The central joist is then cut and the opening trimmed with two trimmers and, if required, an infil joist.

Chimney trimming

52 Where the width of a chimney is greater than the normal spacing between trussed rafters, trusses may have a greater spacing between them in the area of the chimney stack, providing the increased spacing is not more than twice the normal truss spacing.

As per Part L of the Building Regulations, the timbers should be at least 38 mm clear of the chimney stack. Infil rafters, which should be nailed to the side of infil joists and to the wall plate, should be at least 25 mm deeper than trussed rafters to allow for a birdsmouth to be formed at the wall plate.

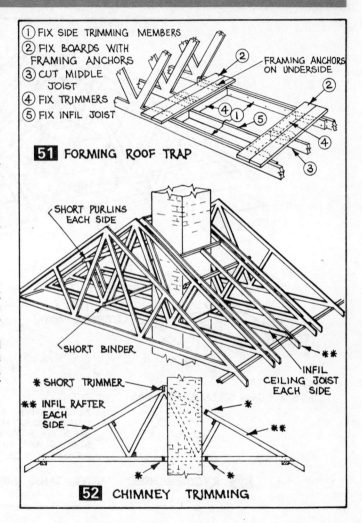

1. FIX SIDE TRIMMING MEMBERS
2. FIX BOARDS WITH FRAMING ANCHORS
3. CUT MIDDLE JOIST
4. FIX TRIMMERS
5. FIX INFIL JOIST

FRAMING ANCHORS ON UNDERSIDE

51 FORMING ROOF TRAP

SHORT PURLINS EACH SIDE

SHORT BINDER

** INFIL RAFTER EACH SIDE

* SHORT TRIMMER

INFIL CEILING JOIST EACH SIDE

52 CHIMNEY TRIMMING

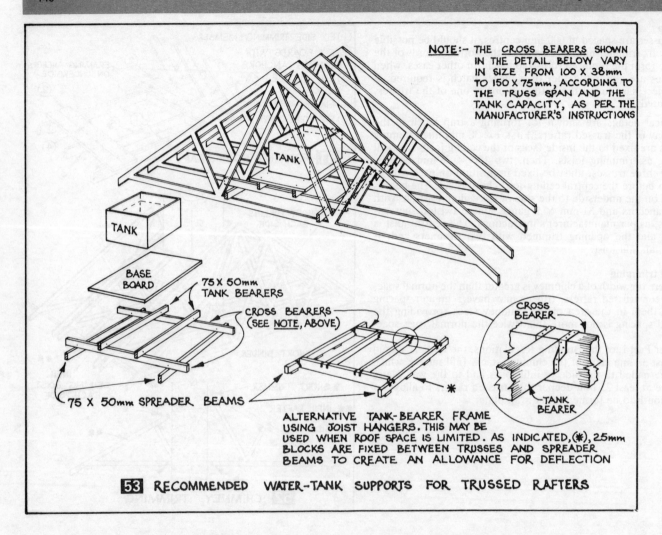

NOTE:– THE CROSS BEARERS SHOWN IN THE DETAIL BELOW VARY IN SIZE FROM 100 X 38mm TO 150 X 75mm, ACCORDING TO THE TRUSS SPAN AND THE TANK CAPACITY, AS PER THE MANUFACTURER'S INSTRUCTIONS

TANK

TANK

BASE BOARD

75 X 50mm TANK BEARERS

CROSS BEARERS (SEE NOTE, ABOVE)

75 X 50mm SPREADER BEAMS

CROSS BEARER

TANK BEARER

ALTERNATIVE TANK-BEARER FRAME USING JOINT HANGERS. THIS MAY BE USED WHEN ROOF SPACE IS LIMITED. AS INDICATED, (✳), 25mm BLOCKS ARE FIXED BETWEEN TRUSSES AND SPREADER BEAMS TO CREATE AN ALLOWANCE FOR DEFLECTION

53 RECOMMENDED WATER-TANK SUPPORTS FOR TRUSSED RAFTERS

FLAT ROOFS

54 The structure of flat roofs is very similar to that used for suspended timber floors, especially when kept level for the provision of a ceiling on the underside. If the ceiling is unimportant, or not required, the joists may be set up out of level to create the necessary *fall* (roof slope). Like floors, the roof joists span across the shortest distance between load-bearing walls – or the longest distance when cross-beams are used – at similar centres to floor joists. They are subject to the same rules as floors regarding strutting being used when the span exceeds 2.5 m. Suitable joist sizes can be obtained either by structural design or by reference to Tables 4 and 5 in Schedule 6 of the Building Regulations.

This form of roof – constructed with timber joists and various types of decking material – has span limitations and is therefore usually restricted to small roofs as on garages and dwelling-house extensions. Other flat roofs may be constructed of reinforced concrete in many forms, including hollow, precast floor beams, etc.

In a level position, the roof joists are either fixed to wall plates by skew-nailing with r.h.w. nails or by framing anchors, with galvanized 'U'-shaped restraint straps fixed over the plates and to the inside face of the wall at maximum 2.0 m centres – or, without wall plates, the joists may be anchored to the tops of the wall with twisted side-fixing restraint straps.

Wedge-shaped timber fillets, or diminishing parallel-fillets, known as firring pieces, are fixed to the upper joist edges to form the necessary *fall* or roof slope. These falls vary between 1 in 40 (25 mm in 1.0 m) and 1 in 80 (25 mm in 2.0 m). Common impervious roof coverings include asbestos-based bitumen felt in the form of three-layer built-up felt and spa chippings – and two- or three-layer mastic asphalt.

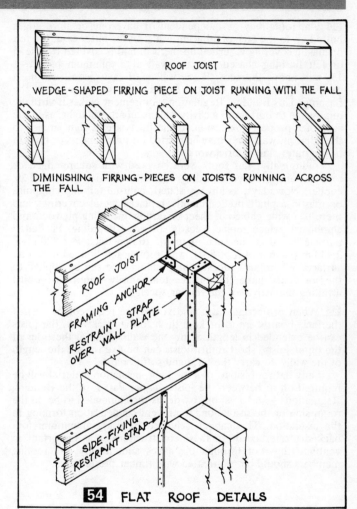

ROOF JOIST

WEDGE-SHAPED FIRRING PIECE ON JOIST RUNNING WITH THE FALL

DIMINISHING FIRRING-PIECES ON JOISTS RUNNING ACROSS THE FALL

ROOF JOIST

FRAMING ANCHOR

RESTRAINT STRAP OVER WALL PLATE

SIDE-FIXING RESTRAINT STRAP

54 FLAT ROOF DETAILS

55 Flat roofs may be independent or have one or more edges butted up to the face of adjacent walls. In the latter case, the felt or mastic covering is turned up the wall and is covered by a lead or felt flashing chased into the wall at a minimum height of 150 mm above the roof. If the wall is of cavity construction, a cavity tray should be inserted to lap onto the top edge of the flashing. This Building Regulation requirement makes it virtually impossible to butt up to a cavity wall as an afterthought, as in the case of a property extension. If the joists are at right angles to the adjacent wall, they may be carried on joist hangers or built in to the outer skin of brickwork.

Traditionally, flat roofs were covered with square-edged or tongued and grooved boarding and covered with lead, zinc or copper. Nowadays, as already stated, built-up felt and chippings or mastic asphalt predominantly replaces metal coverings and there is a wide choice of sheet materials, including plywood and chipboard, which replaces costly softwood boarding. Pre-felted particle board is one such material, 16 mm thick × 1.220 m × 2.440 m (⅝ in × 4 ft × 8 ft), with roofing felt bonded onto one surface. When laid, adhesive and sealing tape can be applied to the joints to make the surface temporarily waterproof whilst awaiting the arrival of the roofing specialist.

56 When projecting eaves and verges are required, or even if the facia boards are to be kept flush to the brickwork, the joists can be extended in length across the walls – and at the sides of the outer joists, short return-joists can be fixed along the length of the walls, to carry the facia and soffit boards.

If any flat roof is part of a dwelling, insulation material will be required on or between the joists, as per Part F of the Building Regulations – and a vapour barrier is recommended to be on the room side of the insulation, to prevent condensation forming in the insulation. This can be achieved by using aluminium foil-backed plasterboard. In these constructions, it is important to ventilate the roof through the eaves and, ideally, the roofing members should be pre-treated with timber preservative.

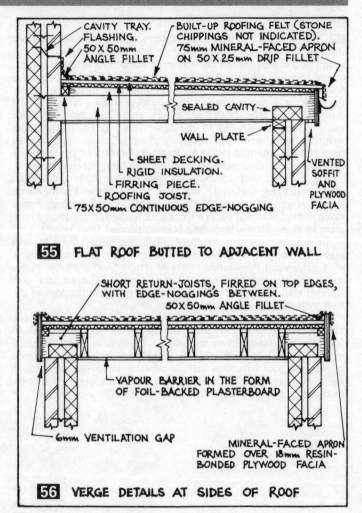

55 FLAT ROOF BUTTED TO ADJACENT WALL

56 VERGE DETAILS AT SIDES OF ROOF

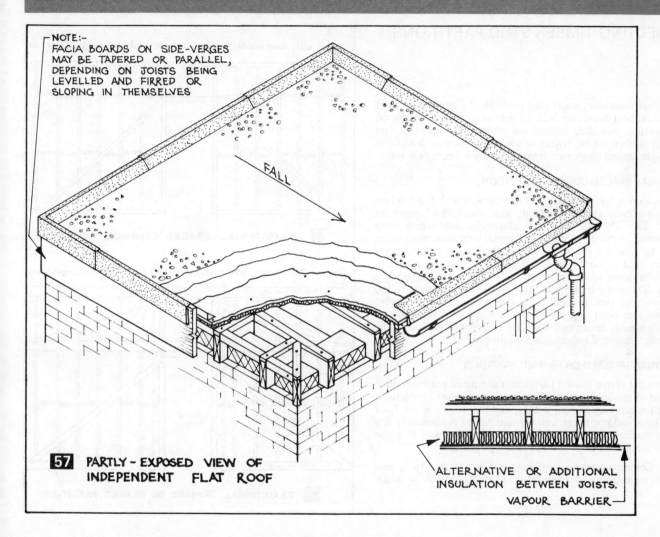

NOTE:-
FACIA BOARDS ON SIDE-VERGES
MAY BE TAPERED OR PARALLEL,
DEPENDING ON JOISTS BEING
LEVELLED AND FIRRED OR
SLOPING IN THEMSELVES

FALL

57 PARTLY-EXPOSED VIEW OF
INDEPENDENT FLAT ROOF

ALTERNATIVE OR ADDITIONAL
INSULATION BETWEEN JOISTS.
VAPOUR BARRIER

13 ERECTING TIMBER STUD PARTITIONS

Partitions are secondary walls used to divide the internal areas of buildings. Although usually built of lightweight building blocks, other materials, including timber, are often used – especially on suspended timber floors, where block partitions would add too much weight unless supported from below by a beam or a wall.

TRADITIONAL BRACED COMMON PARTITION

1 This is shown for reference and comparison with the modern common partition shown overleaf, and the trussed partition shown at **2** . The 100 × 75 mm diagonal braces which were bridle jointed to the upright and horizontal members, were often included to give the partition greater rigidity against sideways movement, and to carry some of the weight from the centre of the partition down to the cill-plate ends, which were housed in the walls. The main frame was through-morticed, tenoned, and pinned (wooden pins or nails); the intermediate uprights were stub-tenoned to head and cill; the door head was splay-housed and stub-tenoned; door posts were dovetailed and pinned to the cill; and the staggered noggings were butt-jointed.

TRADITIONAL TRUSSED OR FRAMED PARTITION

2 As with the above braced partition, the trussed partition, with the advent of modern materials and methods, is now obsolete. It was used for carrying its own weight, and the weight of the floor above. This should be taken into account before commencing any drastic alterations or removal on conversion works – as these partitions are still to be found in older-type buildings.

Note: Common timber partitions are now referred to as *stud* partitions, or *studding* (derived from old English: *studu* = post).

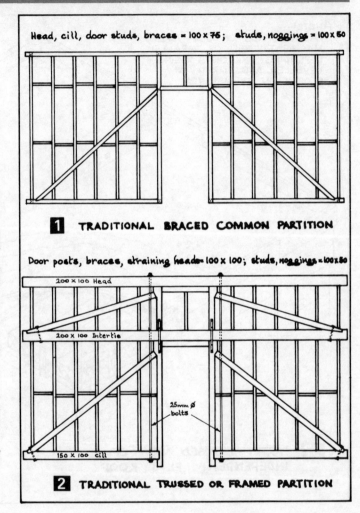

Head, cill, door studs, braces = 100 x 75; studs, noggings = 100 x 50

1 TRADITIONAL BRACED COMMON PARTITION

Door posts, braces, straining heads = 100 x 100; studs, noggings = 100 x 50

200 x 100 Head
200 x 100 Intertie
25mm ø bolts
150 x 100 cill

2 TRADITIONAL TRUSSED OR FRAMED PARTITION

BUILT-UP STUD PARTITION DETAILS

a. Cill (or floor) plate

3 This is cut to length with a crosscut or panel saw, and can be used for setting out the floor position; or the position can be snapped on the floor with a chalk line via tape-rule measurements. The position of any door opening must be deducted from the cill plate setting-out; this is an accumulation of door width (say 762 mm) + door linings (say 28 mm × 2) + 6 mm fitting tolerance + door studs (2 × 50 mm) = 924 mm. The plate is fixed to joists with 100 mm r.h.w. nails, or to floor boards with 75 mm r.h.w. nails, or to concrete floors with plugs and screws, or cartridge-fired masonry nails or bolts, at approximately 900 mm centres (c/c).

b. Head plate

Fix the position by plumbing up to the ceiling from the cill at each end, with a spirit level and straightedge, or plumb bob and line, and then by snapping a chalk line across the ceiling. Cut to length, set out and prop up as shown in **4**, and fix to ceiling joists with 100 mm r.h.w. nails.

c. Wall studs

Mark to length as at **5a** or **5b**, add 1 or 2 mm for a tight fit, cut and fix to brickwork or blockwork with 100 mm cut clasp nails, or plugs and screws, etc. There should be at least three wall fixings, and the ends of studs skew-nailed to the plates **5c**.

d. Door studs

These are now cut, as above, carefully plumbed and fixed. Nail at base into ends of cill with 100 mm r.h.w. nails, then skew-nail at top with 75 mm r.h.w. nails.

e. Door head

Mark position on door studs as in **6**, cut housings 12 mm deep each side, in-situ, working from saw stool or steps. Fix through door studs with 75 mm r.h.w. nails.

f. Intermediate studs

Cut as before for tight fit. Space and fix at 400 mm c/c. skew-nail to head and cill with 75 mm r.h.w. nails as at **7**.

g. Noggings

These are short struts that stiffen up the whole partition. If the

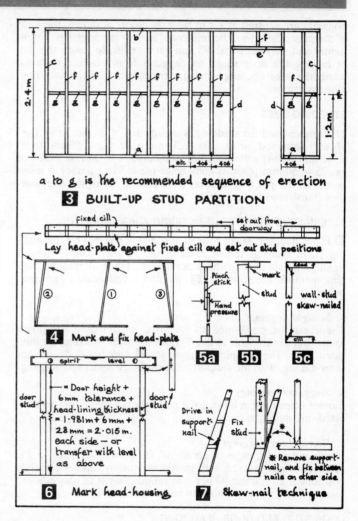

a to g is the recommended sequence of erection

3 BUILT-UP STUD PARTITION

Lay head-plate against fixed cill and set out stud positions

4 Mark and fix head-plate

5a **5b** **5c**

= Door height + 6mm tolerance + head-lining thickness = 1·981m + 6mm + 28mm = 2·015 m. each side — or transfer with level as above

6 Mark head-housing

7 Skew-nail technique

noggings are centred at 1.2 m from the floor, as shown, the joint of the plasterboard will be reinforced against the noggings. Cut in tightly and skew-nail with 75 mm r.h.w. nails; to lessen the risk of bulging the door studs, fix noggings from extreme walls towards the door opening – being extra careful with the final nogging insertions.

STUDDING SIZES

The timber used for studding is usually 100 × 50 mm sawn (*unplaned*) softwood, or ex. 100 × 50 mm p.a.r. (i.e. reduced to 96 × 46 mm *finish*) softwood. For economy, 75 × 50 mm sawn, or ex. 75 × 50 mm p.a.r. is sometimes used. Sawn timber is more common, but p.a.r. is used on some jobs to lessen the irregularities transferred to the surface material.

ALTERNATIVE METHODS OF NOGGING ARRANGEMENTS

8 If possible, successive rows of noggings at 600 mm c/c (between the 1.2 m spacings shown at **3** should be used to give greater rigidity and support to the plasterboard. Three alternative nogging methods are shown at **8**; points for and against are given below.

a. Straight noggings
These can be positioned to reinforce horizontal plasterboard joints, but are difficult to fix. Various methods of fixing are indicated at **a**. The technique shown at **7** can be used here for skew-nailing, with the support-nail positioned under the nogging.

b. Staggered noggings
Cannot effectively reinforce the plasterboard joints, but as indicated, are easier to fix.

c. Herringbone noggings
Positioned at an angle of about 10°, as shown, are easy to fix, achieve a tight fit even with inaccurate cutting, and if correctly positioned, give about 90 per cent reinforcement to plasterboard joints – but have a tendancy to bulge the door studs.

DOOR-STUD AND DOOR-HEAD JOINTS

9 a. Butt-jointed and nailed
Although vertical studs are now usually butt-jointed, the door-head should always be an exception. This inferior method would

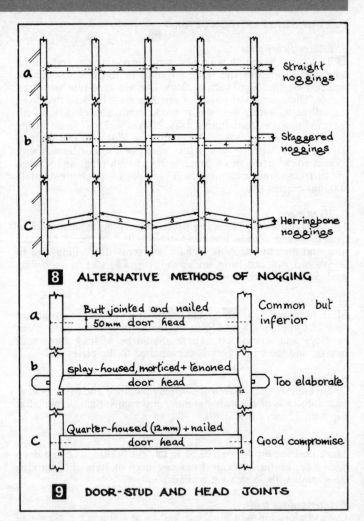

8 ALTERNATIVE METHODS OF NOGGING

a — Straight noggings
b — Staggered noggings
c — Herringbone noggings

a — Butt jointed and nailed — 50mm door head — Common but inferior

b — Splay-housed, morticed + tenoned door head — Too elaborate

c — Quarter-housed (12mm) + nailed door head — Good compromise

9 DOOR-STUD AND HEAD JOINTS

b. Splay-housed, morticed, tenoned and draw-bore wedged
This traditional door-stud/head joint, although ideal for the job, is considered too elaborate and time-consuming nowadays.

c. Quarter-housed (thickness ÷ 4) and nailed
This is the recommended method, as at **3** e, and is a good compromise between the other two extremes.

STUD JOINTS TO CILL AND HEAD PLATE

10 Three methods of jointing vertical studs to the head plate and cill plate have been used, as follows.

a. Stub-tenoned
The short tenons are morticed to half depth into head and cill. This method involves too much hand work on site, and is best suited to preformed partitions being made in the joinery shop, where machinery is available.

b. Housed or trenched
Cut in to a quarter-depth of plate thickness, and skew-nailed at each joint with two 75 mm r.h.w. nails. This method can be easily handled on site – but although housings give the advantage of easier nailing, and straightening and retaining any twisted studs, they are rarely used because of the added time element.

c. Butted and skew-nailed
This is most commonly in use, not because it is the best, but because it is the quickest method of jointing. The stud should be a tight fit, otherwise the strength of this joint is very much impaired. Three 75 mm r.h.w. nails should be used, two in one side, one in the other, as shown previously at **7**. This gives a reasonable chance of correcting any twists in the studs.

DOOR-STUD /CILL-PLATE JOINTS

11 Traditionally these were dovetailed and pinned (dowelled or nailed) as shown, to effectively retain the base of the stud. 100 × 63 mm or 75 mm sawn timber was used.

The presentday method, using 100 × 50 mm sawn timber, is to butt the door stud and nail it against the cill. The nails, 100 mm r.h.w., should be slightly angled to form a dovetail key. This in itself is relatively weak unless, as shown, a central fixing is skew-nailed into the floor on each stud.

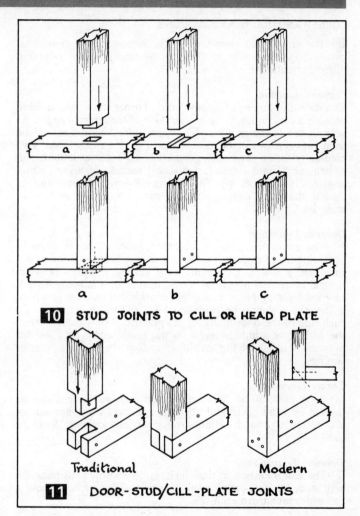

10 STUD JOINTS TO CILL OR HEAD PLATE

Traditional   Modern

11 DOOR-STUD/CILL-PLATE JOINTS

CORNER AND DOORWAY JUNCTIONS

12 The small plan shown at (a) is an uncommon layout for partitioning, but serves to illustrate the four junctions requiring different treatment.

Corner L-junction

Traditionally, three full-length vertical corner studs were used to provide a surface for fixing on each side of the internal angle. As seen in the isometric view (b¹) – small offcut blocks should be used between two of the corner studs, to add rigidity, and give continuity to the rows of noggings. For economy of timber, and to achieve a similar result, a practical method of using *vertical* noggings is shown at (b²). This saves a full-length vertical stud, as usually the extra noggings can be cut from offcuts and waste material.

Doorway L-junction

(c) Where a doorway meets a corner L-junction, the problem of providing fixing surfaces on the internal angle is the same as before, and a similar treatment, using vertical noggings between normal horizontal noggings, is used instead of a full-length stud. In good building practice, another consideration at this junction, is that there should be provision for a full-width architrave on each side of the door-lining leg. In practice, 3 or 4 mm less than the architrave width is given on the inside angle to allow for eventual scribing of the architrave against the irregular plaster surface.

Corner T-junction

(d) As shown, 50 × 25 mm full-length vertical battens can be housed into the horizontal noggings and fixed on either side of the butted wall stud. Alternatively, vertical noggings could be used.

Doorway T-junction

(e) The consideration in this situation, as shown, is to pack the wall stud, (acting here as a sub frame) if necessary, to achieve a full-width architrave each side.

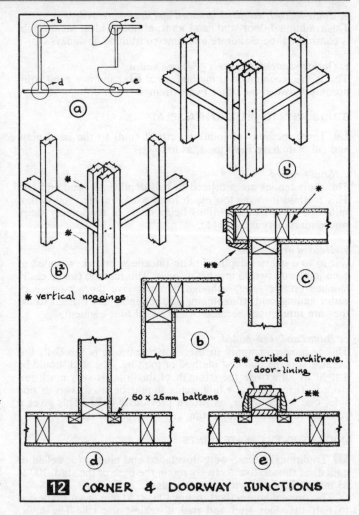

* vertical noggings

** scribed architrave. door-lining

50 x 25mm battens

12 CORNER & DOORWAY JUNCTIONS

FLOOR AND CEILING JUNCTIONS

13a Although common stud partitions do not normally present weight problems on suspended timber floors, certain points must be considered when a partition, running parallel to the joists, ①, rests on the floor boards either in a different position to a joist below, or ②, in a position that coincides with a joist below (both situations inhibit floor-board removal for rewiring, etc. but by virtue of being on the floor boards, the load of the partition is more evenly distributed); or, ③, misses a joist required for head-plate fixings; or, ④, if erected before the ceiling is boarded, creates a problem in board-fixings to the ceiling on each side of the partition.

13b This shows a method of overcoming the lack of head fixings by inserting 100 × 50 mm (or less) noggings between the ceiling joists at about 1 m centres.

13c This shows a method of overcoming all the previous problems, but uses more timber and requires extra work and care at the joisting stage. Arrangements of double ceiling-and-floor joists, with spacing blocks between, are set up. The blocks should be inserted at a maximum of 1 m centres and fixed with 100 mm r.h.w. nails, using staggered side fixings **13e** . To achieve more of a beam effect with the double floor-joists – and so offset the disadvantage of a direct load – the spacing blocks should be replaced by a continuous middle joist, bolted into position with 12 mm diameter bolts, 50 mm diameter or square washers, and 75 mm diameter toothed timber-connectors at 900 mm c/c: **13f**

13d This illustrates a situation that presents no problems, when the partition runs at right angles to the floor and ceiling joists. The cill plate is best fixed on the joists, to allow for expansion and contraction of the floor boards or membrane – hence the 12 mm gap each side – but can be fixed on the boards. The head plate can either be fixed directly to the joists or the boarded ceiling.

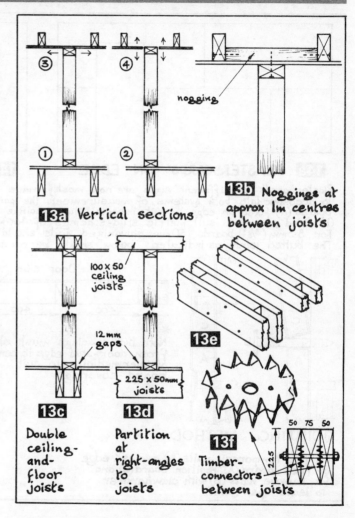

13a Vertical sections

13b Noggings at approx 1m centres between joists

100 × 50 ceiling joists

12 mm gaps

225 × 50mm joists

13c Double ceiling-and-floor joists

13d Partition at right-angles to joists

13e

13f Timber-connectors between joists

50 75 50

225

nogging

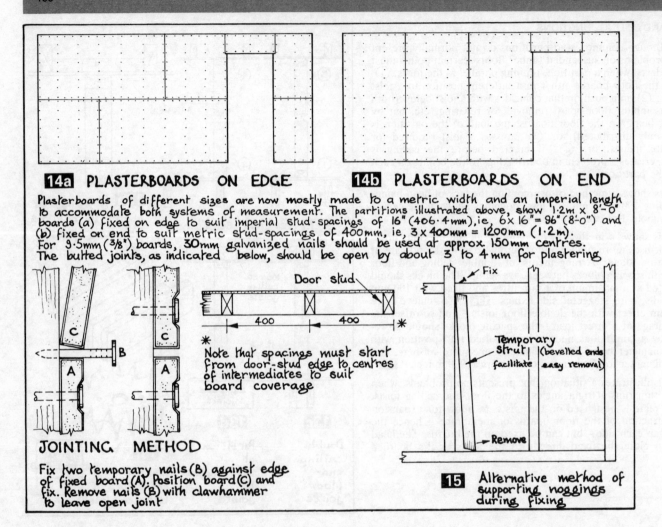

14a PLASTERBOARDS ON EDGE   **14b PLASTERBOARDS ON END**

Plasterboards of different sizes are now mostly made to a metric width and an imperial length to accommodate both systems of measurement. The partitions illustrated above, show 1·2m × 8'-0" boards (a) fixed on edge to suit imperial stud-spacings of 16" (406·4mm), ie, 6 × 16" = 96" (8'-0") and (b) fixed on end to suit metric stud-spacings of 400mm, ie, 3 × 400mm = 1200mm (1·2m). For 9·5mm (³/₈") boards, 30mm galvanized nails should be used at approx. 150mm centres. The butted joints, as indicated below, should be open by about 3 to 4mm for plastering

Door stud

← 400 → ← 400 →   *

* Note that spacings must start from door-stud edge to centres of intermediates to suit board coverage

Fix

Temporary Strut (bevelled ends facilitate easy removal)

← Remove

JOINTING METHOD

Fix two temporary nails (B) against edge of fixed board (A). Position board (C) and fix. Remove nails (B) with clawhammer to leave open joint

15 Alternative method of supporting noggings during fixing

Brick or stone arches over windows and doorways, in a variety of geometrical shapes, can only now be seen mainly on older-type buildings. Presentday design favours straight lines for various reasons, including visual change, cost, and structural requirements in relation to new materials and design. Curved arches have been largely replaced by reinforced concrete boot-lintels, and galvanized, light-weight, pressed-steel lintels as shown at **1b**.

However, arches cannot be regarded as obsolete, and will still be required to match existing work on property maintenance, conversions and extensions.

Arches are built on temporary wooden structures called centres, dealt with in the next chapter. Geometry is required to set out the shape of the centre.

BASIC DEFINITIONS

1a *Springing line* is an imaginary reference or datum line at the base of the arch (where the arch *springs* from). *Span* is the distance between the reveals (sides) of the opening. *Centre line* is an imaginary vertical line equal to half the span. *Rise* is a measurement on the centre line between springing and intrados. *Intrados* or *soffit* refers to the underide of the arch. *Extrados* refers to the topside. The highest area on the extrados is the *crown*. The wedge-shaped units in the arch are called *voussoirs* (pronounced *vooswars*). The central voussoir at the crown is known as the *key* (final insert that *locks* the arch structurally). *Centre* is the pivoting or compass point of the radius. *Radius* is the geometrical distance of the centre point from the concave of a segment or circle.

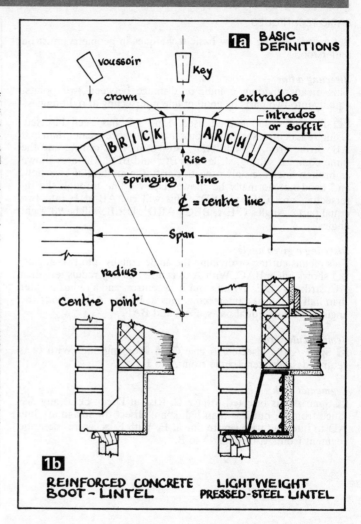

BASIC TECHNIQUES

Before proceeding, a few basic techniques in geometry must be understood.

Bisecting a line

This means dividing a line, or distance between two points, equally into two parts by another line intersecting at right angles.

2a illustrates the method used. Line AB has been bisected. Using A as centre, set the compass to any distance greater than half AB. Strike arcs AC^1 and AD^1. Now using B as centre, and the same compass setting, strike arcs BC^2 and BD^2. The arcs shown as broken lines are only used to clarify the method of bisection, and need not normally be shown. Draw a line through the intersecting arcs C^1C^2 to D^1D^2. This will cut AB at E into two equal parts. Angles C^1EA, BEC^2, AED^1, D^2EB, will be 90° right angles.

Bisecting a given angle

This means cutting or dividing the angle equally into two angles. **2b** shows angle BAC. With A as centre and any radius less than AC, strike arc DE. With D and E as centres, and a radius greater than half DE, strike intersecting arcs at F. Join AF to divide the angle BAC into equal parts, FAC and BAF.

Semi-circular arch

3 Span AB is bisected to give C on springing line. With C as centre, describe semi-circle from A to B.

Segmental arch

4 Span AB is bisected to give C. Rise at D can be at any distance from C, but less than half span. Bisect the imaginary line AD to intersect with centre line at E. With E as centre, describe segment from A, through D to B.

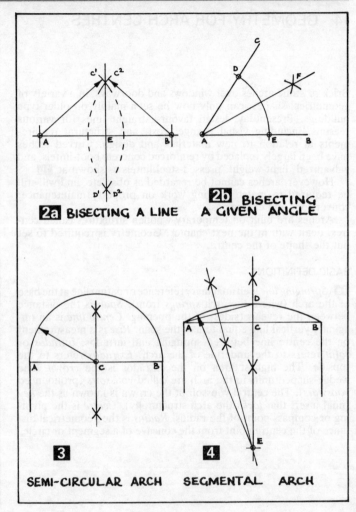

2a BISECTING A LINE

2b BISECTING A GIVEN ANGLE

3 SEMI-CIRCULAR ARCH

4 SEGMENTAL ARCH

Definition of geometrical shapes
Illustrated at **5a** is an explanation for some of the other arch shapes to follow.

Hyperbola: The name given to the curve produced when a cone is cut by a plane (straight, sheet surface) making a larger angle with the base than the side angle of the cone; e.g. 60° cone, 70° to 90° cut.

Parabola: The name given to the curve produced when a cone is cut by a plane parallel to its side; e.g. 60° cone, 60° cut.

Ellipse: The name given to the shape produced when a cone or cylinder is cut by a plane making a smaller angle with the base than the side angle of the cone or cylinder; with the exception that the cutting plane must not be parallel to the base, otherwise true circles will be produced.

Axes of the ellipse
5b An imaginary line through the base and top of a cone or cylinder, that cuts exactly through the centre, is known as an axis. The shape around the axis (centre) is equal in any direction, but when cut by an angled plane – to form an ellipse – the shape enlarges in one direction, according to the angle of cut. For reference, the long and the short lines that intersect through the centre, are called the major axis and the minor axis.

The axes on each side of the central intersection, by virtue of being halved, are called semi-major and semi-minor axes. The semi-elliptical arch is so called because only half of the ellipse is used.

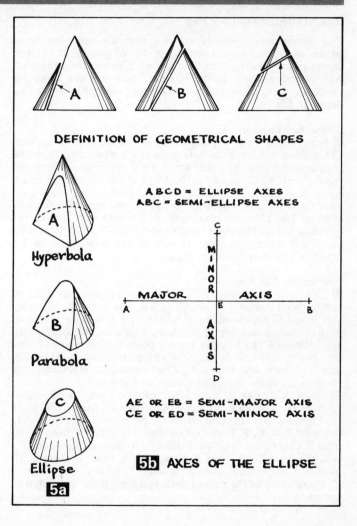

DEFINITION OF GEOMETRICAL SHAPES

Hyperbola

Parabola

Ellipse

ABCD = ELLIPSE AXES
ABC = SEMI-ELLIPSE AXES

MAJOR AXIS
MINOR AXIS

AE OR EB = SEMI-MAJOR AXIS
CE OR ED = SEMI-MINOR AXIS

5a

5b AXES OF THE ELLIPSE

TRUE SEMI-ELLIPTICAL ARCHES

True semi-elliptical shapes are not normally used for brick arches, as the methods of setting out do not give the bricklayer the necessary centre-points as a reference to the radiating normals of the voussoir joints. However, the problem could be solved by using a simple, purpose-made tangent-template, as shown at **6a** .

Intersecting-lines method

6 Span AB, given as the major axis, is bisected at E to produce CD, a lesser amount than AB, given as the minor axis. Vertical lines from AB and horizontal lines from C are drawn to form the rectangle FGAB. Lines AF, GB, AE, and EB are divided by an equal, convenient number of parts. Radiating lines are drawn from C to 1^1, 2^1, 3^1, and so on to 12^1; and from D, through divisions 1 to 12 on the major axis, to intersect with their corresponding radial. These are radials 1 to 1^1, 2 to 2^1, 3 to 3^1, and so on. The intersections plot the path of the semi-ellipse to be drawn freehand or by other means.

Intersecting-ARCS method

7 Draw the major axis (AB) and the semi-minor axis (CE) as before. With compass set to AE or EB, and C as centre, strike arcs F and G on the major axis; these are known as the *focal points*. Mark a number of points anywhere on the semi-major axis between F and E; place the first point very close to F. Number these points 1, 2, 3, etc. Now with compass set to A1, strike arcs H^1 from F, and J^1 from G. Reset compass to B1, strike arcs H^1 from G, and J^1 from F. Continue as follows:
Compass A2, strike K^2 from F, L^2 from G. Compass B2, strike K^2 from G, L^2 from F. Compass A3, strike M^3 from F, N^3 from G. Compass B3, strike M^3 from G, N^3 from F. Compass A4, strike O^4 from F, P^4 from G. Compass B4, strike O^4 from G, P^4 from F. Compass A5, strike Q^5 from F, R^5 from G. Compass B5, strike Q^5 from G, R^5 from F. Compass A6, strike S^6 from F, T^6 from G. Compass B6, strike S^6 from G, T^6 from F.

These arcs plot the path of the semi-ellipse to be completed as before.

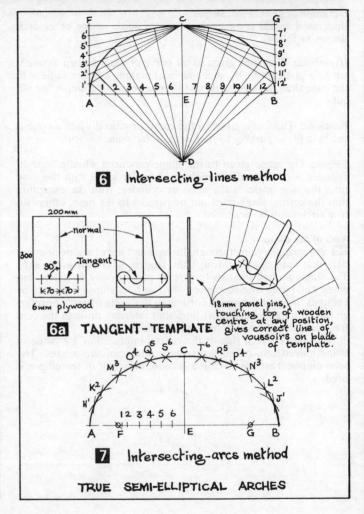

6 Intersecting-lines method

6a TANGENT-TEMPLATE

18mm panel pins, touching top of wooden centre at any position, gives correct line of voussoirs on blade of template.

7 Intersecting-arcs method

TRUE SEMI-ELLIPTICAL ARCHES

Concentric-circles method

8 Draw the major axis (AB) and the semi-minor axis (CE) as before. Strike semi-circles EA and EC. Draw any number of radiating lines from E to cut both semi-circles. For convenience, the angles of the radials used at **8** are 15°, 30°, 45°, 60°, and 75°, each side of the centre line CE. Draw vertical lines inwards from points 1, 2, 3, etc. on the outer semi-circle, and horizontal lines outwards from points 11, 12, 13, etc. on the inner semi-circle. These intersections at points 0, plot the path of the semi-ellipse to be drawn freehand or by other means.

Short-trammel method

9 Draw major and semi-minor axes as before. Select a thin lath or similar as a trammel rod. Mark it as shown, with the semi-major axis (A^1E^1) and the semi-minor axis (C^1E^1). Rotate the trammel in a variety of positions similar to that shown, ensuring that marks E^1E^2 always touch the two axes, and mark off sufficient points at A^1C^1 to plot the path of the semi-ellipse to be completed as before.

Long-trammel method

10 Similar to previous method, except that semi-major and semi-minor axes form a continuous measurement on the trammel; the outer marks thereon move along the axes, while the inner mark (0) plots the path of the semi-ellipse. This method is better than the previous when the difference in length between the two axes is only slight.

Pin-and-string method

11 Uses focal points F and G on the major axis, equalling AE or EB on the compass, struck from C. Drive a nail into points FCG. Pass a piece of string around the three nails and tie tightly. Cut a notch in a pencil, (C^1), remove nail at C, replace with pencil and rotate to left and right, as shown at HIJ, to produce semi-ellipse.

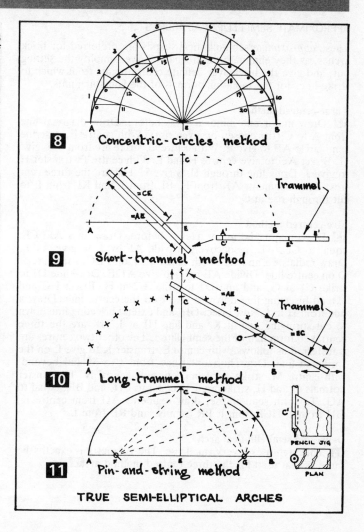

8 Concentric-circles method

9 Short-trammel method

10 Long-trammel method

11 Pin-and-string method

PENCIL JIG

PLAN

TRUE SEMI-ELLIPTICAL ARCHES

APPROXIMATE SEMI-ELLIPTICAL ARCHES

These *approximate* semi-elliptical shapes are preferred for brick arches, as they eliminate the freehand curve, simplify the setting out, and give the bricklayer definite centre points from which to strike lines for the radiating normals of the voussoir joints.

Three-centred method

12 Draw major and minor axes as before. Draw diagonal line from A to C (the chosen or given rise). With centre E, describe semi-circle AB to give F. With centre C, strike arc from F to give G. Bisect AG to give centres H and I. With centre E, transfer H to give J. Draw line through IJ to give L. HIJ are the three centres. Draw segments AK from H, BL from J, and KL from I, to cut through rise at C.

Five-centred method

13 Draw major and minor axes as before. Draw lines AF, CF, equal to CE, AE, respectively. Divide AF by 3, to give A12F. Draw radials C1 and C2. With centre E, radius EC, strike arc at D on centre line. Divide AE by 3, to give A12E. Draw line D1 to strike C1 at G, and line D2 to strike C2 at H. Bisect HC and extend bisecting line down to give I on the centre line. Draw a line from H to I. Now bisect GH, and extend bisecting line down to cut springing line at K, and line HI at J. IJK are the three centres to form half of the semi-ellipse. The other two centres are transferred as follows: with centre E, transfer K to give L on the springing line. Draw horizontal line from J to M and beyond; with centre M, strike arc from J to give centre N. To transfer normals G and H, strike arc CP, equal to CH, and BR, equal to AG. To form semi-ellipse, draw segments AG from centre K, GH from J, HCP from I, PR from N, and RB from L.

Depressed semi-elliptical arch

14 This arch uses a very small rise. The geometry is exactly the same as that used for the three-centred method at **12** .

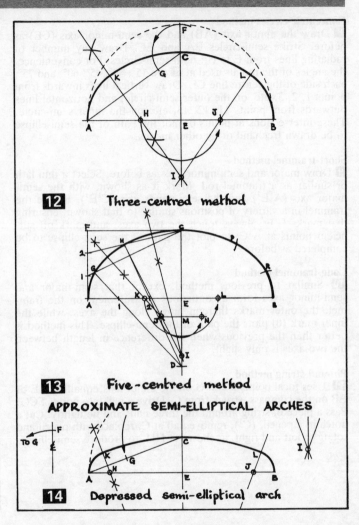

12 Three-centred method

13 Five-centred method

APPROXIMATE SEMI-ELLIPTICAL ARCHES

14 Depressed semi-elliptical arch

Equilateral Gothic arch

15 The radius of this arch, equal to the span, is struck from centres A and B to a point C. Imaginary lines AB, BC, CA, are equal to each other in length and contain three angles of 60°. Line AD is the geometrical *normal* to the curve, and a line at right angles to this is known as a *tangent*. Normals EFGHIJKL, etc. are indicated by broken lines to form the voussoirs of the arch.

Depressed Gothic arch

16 (Sometimes called 'obtuse' or 'drop' Gothic arch.) The centres for this arch come within the span, on the springing line. Bisect AB to give centre line through E. With compass less than AB, strike rise at C from A. (Alternatively, mark chosen or given rise at C from E). Draw line AC and bisect to give centre F on the springing line. With centre E, transfer F to give centre G. Strike segments AC from F, and BC from G.

Lancet Gothic arch

17 The centres for this type of arch are outside the span, on the springing line. Bisect AB to give centre line through E. With compass more than AB, strike rise at C from A. (Or mark known rise at C from E). Draw line AC and bisect to give centre F on extended springing line. With centre E, transfer F to give centre G. Strike segments AC from F, and BC from G.

(*Note*: Line AC in the above arches is optional, and need not actually be drawn.)

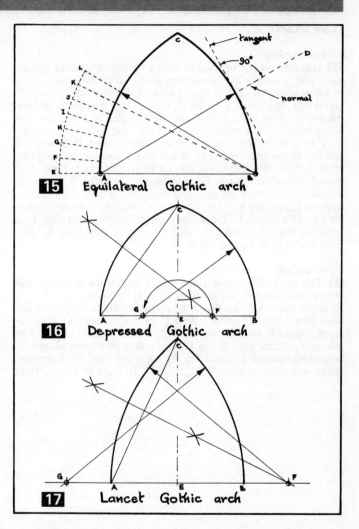

15 Equilateral Gothic arch

16 Depressed Gothic arch

17 Lancet Gothic arch

Tudor arches

Variable method

18 This method can be used to meet a variety of given or chosen rises, and is usually mastered when practised a few times.

Draw span AB. Bisect to give extended centre line through E and down. Mark rise at C. Draw vertical line AF, equal to two-thirds rise (CE). Join F to C. At right angles to FC, draw line down from C. With compass equal to AF, and A as centre, transfer F to give G. With same compass setting, mark H from C on line CI. Draw line from G to H and bisect; extend bisecting line down until it intersects with line CI to give centre I. Draw line from I, extended through G on springing line. With E as centre, transfer G to give J on springing line. Again with E as centre, transfer I, through K, to strike arc at L. With K as centre, transfer I to give centre L. Draw line from L to extend through J on springing line. To complete, strike segments AM from G, MC from I, CN from L, and NB from J.

Fixed method

19 This method is simpler, and can be used when the rise is not critical, and the only information given is the span.

Draw span AB and divide by 4 to give DEF. Draw vertical lines down from D and F. With D as centre, transfer F to intersect vertical line, giving G. With F as centre, transfer D to intersect vertical line, giving H. Draw diagonals from H and G, extending through D and F on the springing line. To complete, strike segments AI from D, IC from H, BJ from F, and JC from G.

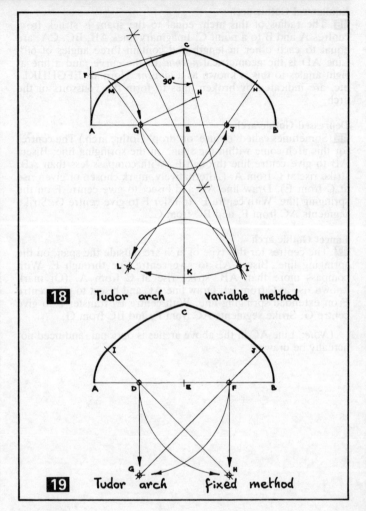

18 Tudor arch   variable method

19 Tudor arch   fixed method

Depressed Tudor arch

20 Draw span AB and divide by 6 to give DEFGH. Draw vertical lines down from E and G. With centre D, transfer H down to O, and with centre H, transfer D down to O. Draw diagonal normals through DO and HO, extending down to intersect vertical lines at K and L, and extending up past the springing line to I and J. To complete, strike segments AI from D, IC from L, BJ from H, and JC from K.

Note: Division of span can be varied to achieve a different visual effect; so can the angles of the normals at D and H, drawn here at 60°. For example, 75° would make the arch more depressed.

Straight-top Tudor arch

21 Draw span AB and divide by 9. Mark one-ninth of span from A to give D, and one-ninth from B to give E. Set diagonal normals passing through D and E at 78° to the horizontal. With centre D, strike arch curve AF, and with centre E, strike BG. From F and G, draw straight arch lines at 90° from normals, to intersect at crown C.

Note: Positions of centres D and E can be varied to achieve a different visual effect; so can the 78° angles of the normals – but the arch top must always be tangential (at 90°) to the normals.

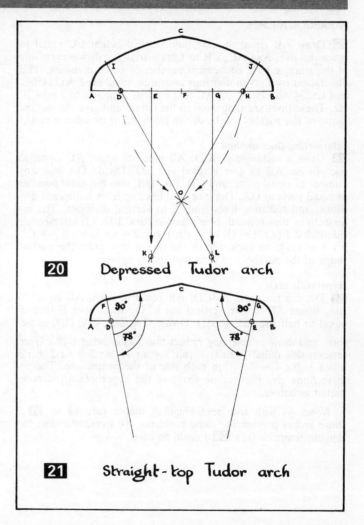

20 Depressed Tudor arch

21 Straight-top Tudor arch

PARABOLIC ARCHES

22 Draw AB equal to span, and vertical height EC equal to twice the rise. Join AC, CB to form a triangle; divide each side of the triangle by a convenient number of equal divisions. This illustration uses seven divisions each side, numbered A123456C, and C123456B. Join 1 on AC to 1 on CB, 2 on AC to 2 on CB, etc. These lines are tangential to the curve, and give the outline shape of the parabola to be drawn freehand or by other means.

Intersecting-lines method

23 Draw a rectangle ABCD. AB equal to span, AC equal to rise. Bisect AB to give vertical line EO. Divide OA into any number of equal parts, and OB, CA, DB, into the same number of equal parts as OA. Draw vertical lines up from horizontal divisions, and radiating lines from E to vertical divisions. The intersections thus formed, being base-vertical 1 (b.v.l) intersecting side-radial 1 (s.r.l) = (b.v.l ÷ s.r.l), b.v.2 ÷ s.r.2, b.v.3 ÷ s.r.3, b.v.4 ÷ s.r.4, on each side of the centre line, gives the outline shape of the parabola to be completed as before.

Hyperbolic arch

24 Draw a rectangle ABCD. AB equal to span, AC equal to rise. Bisect AB to give vertical line EFO. Make apex E from F equal to half rise (EF = $\frac{FO}{2}$). Divide OA, OB, CA, DB, as before, and draw intersecting radials thus: base-radial 1 (b.r.l) intersects side-radial 1 (s.r.l) = (b.r.1 ÷ s.r.1), b.r.2 ÷ s.r.2, b.r.3 ÷ s.r.3, b.r.4 ÷ s.r.4, on each side of the centre line. The intersections give the outline shape of the hyperbola to be completed as before.

Note: As with true semi-elliptical shapes (see **6** to **11**) these arches present the same problems. To overcome this, the tangent-template (see **6a**) could be used.

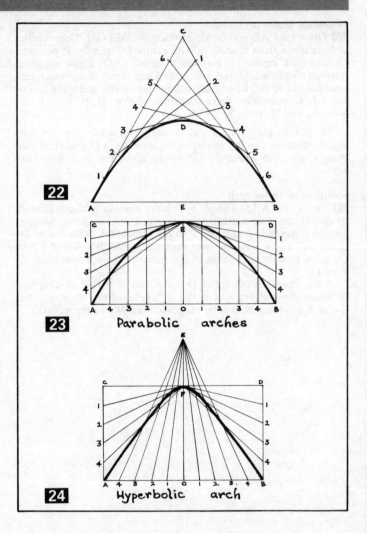

22

23 Parabolic arches

24 Hyperbolic arch

15 MAKING AND FIXING ARCH CENTRES

The temporary wooden structures upon which brick arches are formed, are known as *centres*. They can be made in the joinery shop – taking advantage of available machinery – or on site. The construction of the centre can be simple or complex, depending mainly on two factors: the span of the opening, and how many times the centre is to be used for other arches.

For small spans up to about 1.2 m, the centre can be simple, of single-rib, twin-rib, or four-rib construction. For spans exceeding 1.2 m, the centre becomes more complex, of multi-rib construction.

1 A *beam compass* or *radius rod* is required to set out the full-size shape of the centre, either directly onto the rib material (single and twin-rib) or onto a hardboard or plywood setting-out board, (four-rib and multi-rib centres) from which a template is made of the common rib shape.

The beam compass consists of trammel heads and a length of timber, say 38 × 18 mm, known as a beam. To improvise, a radius rod can be easily made, consisting of a timber lath with a panel pin or nail through one end, the other end drilled to hold a pencil firmly.

SINGLE-RIB, SOLID TURNING PIECE

2 Can be used for segmental arches with small rises up to about 75 mm. Sometimes the rise is so slight (e.g. 10 mm rise, 900 mm span) that a radius rod would not be convenient for drawing the curve, and a triangular frame or trammel rod is used as shown at **2a** . The curve is best cut with a narrow band-saw machine, or, if by hand, with a compass saw or as shown at **2b** , with a cross-cut saw making a series of tangential cuts, then shaped with a compass plane or smoothing plane.

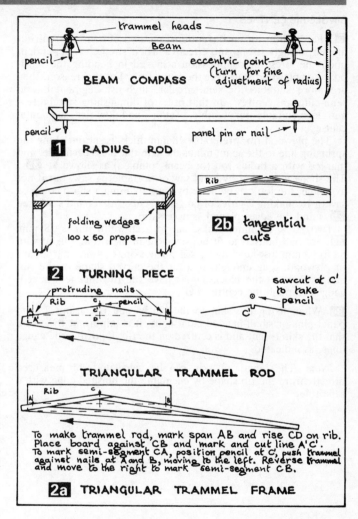

trammel heads

Beam

pencil

eccentric point (turn for fine adjustment of radius)

BEAM COMPASS

pencil

panel pin or nail

1 RADIUS ROD

folding wedges

100 × 50 props

Rib

2b tangential cuts

2 TURNING PIECE

protruding nails

Rib   C   pencil

A   C'   D   B

sawcut at C' to take pencil

C'

TRIANGULAR TRAMMEL ROD

Rib   c

A   c'   B

To make trammel rod, mark span AB and rise CD on rib. Place board against CB and mark and cut line A'C'. To mark semi-segment CA, position pencil at C', push trammel against nails at A and B, moving to the left. Reverse trammel and move to the right to mark semi-segment CB.

2a TRIANGULAR TRAMMEL FRAME

SINGLE-RIB CENTRES

3 These follow an unconventional method of construction, but are surprisingly strong and effective. Their strength is dependent upon the stress of compression achieved in bending the hardboard or plywood skin over the curved rib. For this reason, they are more suitable for semi-circular, high-rise segmental, and semi-elliptical centres – in that order of diminishing suitability – and less suitable for Gothic, Tudor, and low-rise segmental centres.

The plywood rib, preferably 18 mm thick, is set out along the springing line to the span, minus the skin thickness each side, and marked with a radius rod (or beam compass) as shown at **3a** The shape is best cut by band saw or portable jig saw, but if not available, the job can be done by hand by using a sharp compass saw or by making a series of tangential cuts with a hand saw, (see **2b**) and the edges planed as necessary.

Two 50 × 50 mm blocks, cut to arch-width minus 18 mm, **3b**, are half-housed to fit housings cut in the rib and fixed with 50 to 63 mm lost-head nails, **3c** . The skin, of 4 mm hardboard or plywood, long enough to cover the curved shape of the rib, and as wide as the blocks, must have the rib thickness pencil-gauged through the centre, **3d** .

3e When fixing the skin to the blocks and rib, using 25 mm panel pins or small-headed clout nails, it is important to ensure that the skin is taut and is centred on the rib, following the gauge lines, as indicated.

Note: The length of skin can be calculated, or measured directly from the rib shape by encircling the finished edge with a tape rule.

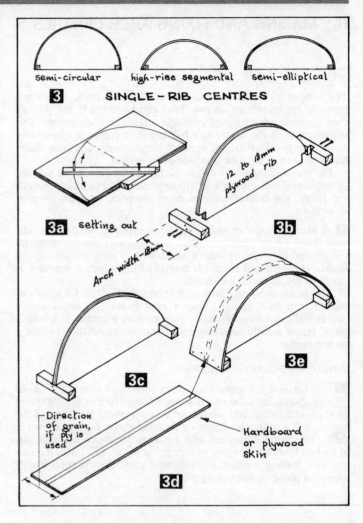

semi-circular   high-rise segmental   semi-elliptical

3   SINGLE-RIB CENTRES

3a   setting out

12 to 18mm plywood rib   **3b**

Arch width-18mm

3c   **3e**

Direction of grain, if ply is used

Hardboard or plywood skin

3d

TWIN-RIB CENTRES

4 These are superior to single-rib centres, and suitable for all arch shapes. The ribs may consist of 12 or 18 mm plywood. Bearers, of 75 × 25 mm or 100 × 25 mm section, are fixed to the underside of each end. These act as spacers between the two ribs, and as bearers supporting the centre on the props. A bracing-spacer, as indicated at **4a**, can be inserted to keep the ribs initially parallel and square. The centre is covered with a hardboard or plywood skin **4b**, or alternatively with strips of timber, known as *laggings*, **4c**. These can be placed close together, referred to as *close-lagging*, or be spaced apart, **4d**, referred to as *open-lagging*.

Close-lagging should be used for gauged arches (tapered voussoirs), and open-lagging for common arches (ordinary bricks used as parallel voussoirs).

To make the centre, set out and form rib as before. Use first rib as template to mark out and form second rib. Cut the two bearers, ex. 75 × 25 mm × arch width minus 18 mm, and fix to underside of ribs at each end with 50 mm round-head or lost-head wire nails; cut and fix bracing-spacer, **4a**. Cut hardboard or plywood skin to width and fix to ribs **4e**, or cut laggings and fix to ribs with 38 or 50 mm lost-head oval nails.

Note: **4f** shows a plan view of a simple jig for cutting the lagging lengths quickly. Two battens are fixed to a bench or stool top. A nail at one end positions the lagging without trapping sawdust; the saw at the other end cuts the required length repeatedly after feeding in the strip towards the nail.

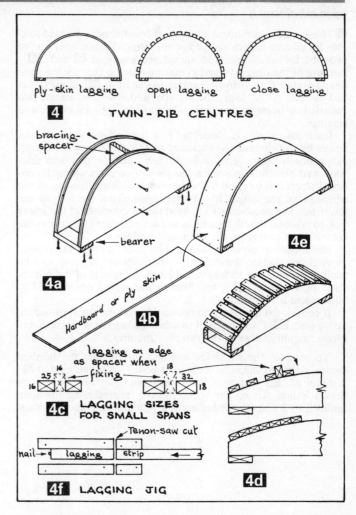

ply-skin lagging   open lagging   close lagging

4 TWIN-RIB CENTRES

bracing-spacer

bearer

4a

Hardboard or ply skin

4b

4e

lagging on edge as spacer when fixing

16 25 16 18 32 18

4c LAGGING SIZES FOR SMALL SPANS

Tenon-saw cut

nail   lagging   strip

4f LAGGING JIG

4d

FOUR-RIB CENTRES

5 These follow traditional methods of construction, and are suitable for all arch shapes except low rise; which require only one or two ribs for small spans, as shown previously at **2** and **4d** . Because of the time involved in making four-rib centres, they are less favoured than twin-rib centres. As seen at **5a** in elevation and section A–A, four ribs are required, two tie beams, two collars, two bearers, two optional struts, an optional brace, and laggings.

Each pair of ribs is connected to a top collar and bottom tie beam, by clench-nails. As indicated at **5b** the nails when driven in, purposely protrude by at least 6 mm, and are then bent sideways and clenched to secure the joint. For extra strength, optional struts can be fixed from the birdsmouth at the apex of the ribs, against the collar, to a central position on the face of the lower tie. The two bearers are fixed to the extremes of the lower ties, to position the rib structures and act as bearers to support the centre when resting on the props and wedges.

Hardboard or plywood skins can be used to cover the centre, in single or double thicknesses – or traditional laggings can be used, efficiently cut to length as before, by means of the improvised jig shown at **4f** , and fixed to the curved ribs with 38 to 50 mm lost-head oval nails.

If considered necessary an optional brace, indicated in section A–A (see **5a**), can be used to achieve squareness in width and greater rigidity between the two rib structures.

To produce the rib shape and also ensure that the finished centre is true to shape, a setting-out board (as mentioned at **1**) is required. **5c** indicates the setting out. The first line to be drawn is line AB on the springing line, representing the span minus 2 to 3 mm (the reduction is a practical tolerance to allow

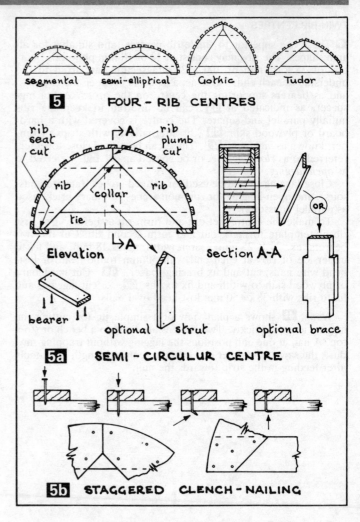

segmental   semi-elliptical   Gothic   Tudor

5 FOUR - RIB CENTRES

rib seat cut
rib plumb cut
rib   collar   rib
tie

Elevation

bearer

Section A-A

optional strut   optional brace

5a SEMI - CIRCULUR CENTRE

5b STAGGERED CLENCH - NAILING

for brick reveals being slightly out of square). Next, bisect line AB to produce centre line CD. Then set beam compass or radius rod to AD and describe semi-circle ACB. Reset compass or radius rod to AD minus lagging thickness, and describe second semi-circle, producing A′, C′, and B′, representing the rib curve. Measure down at least 60 mm from C′ to G, depth of plumb cut; and measure inwards at least 60 mm from A′ to E, and B′ to F, length of seat cuts. Draw tangential lines EG and GF to represent the underside of the ribs. Draw two lines parallel to the springing, to represent top collar and bottom tie beam. (These should be about 100 to 150 mm wide × 25 mm thickness.)

The ribs, as shown at **5d**, can be cut from a 150 × 25 mm or 225 × 25 mm board. A hardboard template **5e** facilitates the marking out of the ribs onto the board economically. To make the template, lay a piece of hardboard on the setting-out board, as shown by the dotted outline at **5c**, strike radius rod from centre D to describe quadrant A′C′, mark plumb cut CG, seat cut AE, remove and cut to shape.

5f shows the marking out of the collar and tie. These are laid in position on setting-out board and marked with radius rod A′D from centre D′, squared up from D. As shown, a small temporary wooden block can be fixed to the tie, to retain the point of the radius rod.

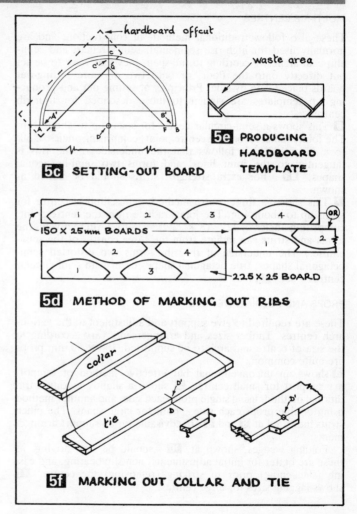

5c SETTING-OUT BOARD

5e PRODUCING HARDBOARD TEMPLATE

5d METHOD OF MARKING OUT RIBS

150 × 25mm BOARDS

225 × 25 BOARD

5f MARKING OUT COLLAR AND TIE

MULTI-RIB CENTRES

These also follow traditional methods of construction, and are normally used for high-rise segmental, semi-circular, and semi-elliptical arches. According to the span, they may have to be set out directly onto the floor, or onto two or more setting-out boards placed side by side. Principles of setting out and producing rib templates are similar to those described for four-rib centres.

6 This shows a semi-circular centre for spans up to about 4 m. The joints radiate from the centre point, comprising angles of 30° (6 × 30° = 180°). It follows that the underside of the ribs is tangential to the joint lines, and forms two semi-hexagonal shapes, **6a** . For extra strength, struts should be added as shown.

7 This shows a three-centre method, semi-elliptical centre for spans up to about 4 m. The joints radiate from the centre point, comprising angles of 22½° (8 × 22½° = 180°). (Alternatively, the joints and struts can radiate from the three centres of the semi-ellipse.) The underside of the ribs forms two distorted semi-octagonal shapes; true octagonal shapes occur with semi-circular centres – see **7a** .

PROPS AND FOLDING WEDGES

These are required to give support and adjustment to the various arch centres. Timber sizes and arrangements vary according to the size of centre and arch to be supported. 100 × 50 mm props are quite common.

8 shows an unconventional but effective method of temporary support for small centres. **9** shows a slightly modified traditional method, using single props each side; and another method using double props each side – both for large spans. The pinch struts indicated at **8** and **9** are advisable for all support arrangements.

Folding wedges, shown at **10** , should be slow-driving, as these are better for initial adjustments, non-slip bearing, and easing (slackening) prior to striking (removing) the centre. **11** shows lagging sizes for large centres.

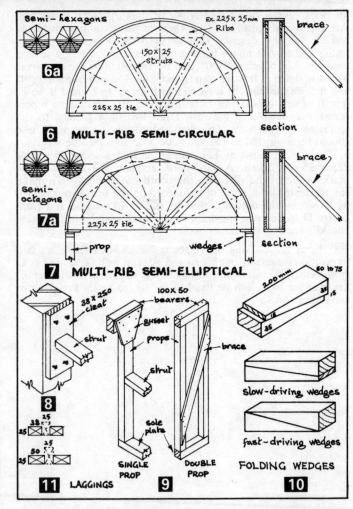

semi-hexagons
6a
Ex. 225 × 25mm Ribs
150 × 25 struts
225 × 25 tie
brace
section
6 MULTI-RIB SEMI-CIRCULAR

semi-octagons
7a
225 × 25 tie
prop
wedges
brace
section
7 MULTI-RIB SEMI-ELLIPTICAL

38 × 250 cleat
strut
8
38
25
25
50
25

100 × 50 bearers
gusset
props
strut
brace
sole plate
SINGLE PROP
DOUBLE PROP
9

11 LAGGINGS

200 mm
50 to 75
35
15
18
35
slow-driving wedges
fast-driving wedges
FOLDING WEDGES
10

APPENDIX
GLOSSARY OF TERMS

The terms and other technical names listed for explanation, are relevant to those used in this book only – not to the industry as a whole – and for continuity, some terms are explained in each chapter and may or may not be repeated here.

Aggregate: Stone, flint and finer particles used in concrete.

Apron lining: A horizontal board, covering the rough-sawn vertical face of a trimmer or trimming joist in a stairwell.

Architrave: A plain or fancy moulding, mitred and fixed around the face-edges of door openings, etc. to add a visual finish and to cover the joint between plaster and door frame or lining.

Arris, arrises: The sharp edges on timber or other material.

Balusters: Lathe-turned wooden posts, fixed between the handrail and string capping or handrail and landing nosing, as part of the balustrade of a staircase.

Baluster sticks: As above, but square posts with no turning.

Balustrade: The barrier at the open side of a staircase or landing, comprising newel posts, handrail and balusters or balustrade rails.

Balustrade rails: Wide rails with less than 100 mm gaps between, fixed below and parallel to handrails, as a modern alternative to an infill of balusters on a staircase.

Bare-faced tenon: A tenon with only one shoulder.

Bearer: A batten that supports a shelf, etc.

Bearing: The point of support for a beam, lintel or joist, etc.

Bed, bedding or bed joint: A controlled thickness of mortar beneath timber plates and bricks, etc.

Birdsmouth: A vee-shaped notch in timber, that is thought to represent a bird's mouth in appearance.

Bits: Tang-ended tools that fit the carpenter's brace for drilling, screwing, countersinking, etc.

Block partitions: Partition walls built of aerated insulation blocks, usually measuring 450 mm long × 215 mm high × 100 mm thick.

Bow: A segmental warp in the length of a board, springing from the wide face of the material.

Boxwood: A yellow-coloured hardwood with close, dense grain – still used in the manufacture of four-fold rules.

Brace: (1) A diagonal support; (2) A tool for holding and revolving a variety of drill bits, etc.

Brad head: Head of nail (oval brad) or awl (bradawl) whose shape is scolloped from the round or oval to a flat point.

Bullnose step: A step at the bottom of a flight of steps, with a quadrant (quarter of a circle) shaped end.

Burr: A sharp metal edge in the form of a lip, projecting from the true arris of the metal.

Butt-joint: A square side-to-side, end-to-end or end-to-side abutment in timber, without any overlapping.

Casement: Hinged or fixed sash windows in a casement frame.

Centimetre: One hundredth of a metre, i.e. ten millimetres (10 mm).

Chamfer: An equal bevel (45° × 45°) removed from the arrises of bearers or slatted shelves, etc.

Chase; chased; chasing: Rough channels or grooves cut in walls or concrete floors to accommodate pipes, conduits or cables; or cut in the face of mortar beds to take the top-turned edge of apron flashings.

Chord: A British Standards' Codes of Practice reference (CP 112 : Part 3 : 1973) to trussed-rafter rafters (top chord) and ceiling-joist ties (bottom chord).

Chuck: The jaws of a brace or drill.

Cladding: The 'clothing' of a structure in the form of relatively thin skin – such as plywood or weather-boarding, etc.

Cleats: Short boards or battens, usually fixed across the grain of other boards to give laminated support to the join.

Clench-nailed: Two pieces of cross-grained timber held together by nails with about 6 to 10 mm of projecting point bent over and flattened on the timber, in the direction of the grain.

Coach bolt: This has a thread, nut and washer at one end and a dome-shaped head and partly square shank at the other. The square portion of shank is hammered into the round hole to stop the bolt turning whilst being tightened.

Common brickwork: Rough brickwork to be plastered or covered.

Concave: Shaped like the inside of a sphere.

Concentric: Sharing the same centre point.

Conduit: A metal pipe for housing electrical cables; although nowadays plastic and fibre tubes are also used.

Convex: Shaped like the outside of a sphere.

Corbel or corbelling: A structural projection from the face of a wall in the form of stone, concrete or stepped brickwork, to act as a bearing for wall plates and purlins, etc.; also, straight or hooked metal corbel plates, being the forerunner of modern joist hangers, were used at about 1.0 m centres, projecting from the face of a wall, to support suspended wall plates.

Course: One rise of bricks or blocks laid in a row.

Cramp: (1) sash cramp: A device for holding timber, etc. together under pressure – usually whilst being glued; **(2) frame cramp or tie:** A galvanized steel bracket holding-device, fixed to the sides of frames and bedded in the mortar joint.

Cross-halving: A half-lap joint between crossed timbers.

Cup or cupping: Concave or convex distortion across the face of a board, usually caused by the board's face being tangential to the growth rings.

Datum: A fixed and reliable reference point from which all levels or measurements are taken, to avoid cumulative errors.

Deadman's finger: A piece of timber for supporting short ends of wood being axed. (See **31**, Ch. 2.)

Decimetre: One-tenth of a metre, i.e. one-hundred millimetres (100 mm).

Dihedral angle: The angle produced between two surfaces, or geometric planes, at the point where they meet. For example, two vertical surfaces meeting at right angles to each other, produce a dihedral angle of 90°, but incline the surfaces from their vertical state, to represent a hip or valley formation, and the dihedral angle thus produced is different, according to the degree of inclination.

Door joint: The necessary gap of 2 to 3 mm around the edges of a door for opening clearances.

Dovetail key: The locking effect of a dovetail, or nails driven in to form a dovetail shape.

Dowel: A round wooden or metal pin.

Draw-bore pin: A front-tapered wooden dowel, driven into an offset hole drilled (separately) through a mortice and tenon joint, to pull up the shoulder fit and permanently reinforce the joint.

Easing: (1) Removing shavings from an edge to achieve a better fit; (2) Concave and convex shaping of stair-string and skirting junctions.

Eaves: The lowest edge of a roof, which usually overhangs the structure from as little as the facia-board thickness up to about 450 mm, and where rainwater drainage is effected via a system of guttering and downpipes.

Eccentric point: The bent portion of a trammel-head pin, which causes the axis (centre) of the pin to move, when rotated, in an eccentric orbit, even though the pin-pointed position remains concentric. This allows fine adjustments to be made to the trammel distance without altering the trammel head.

Facework or face brickwork: Good-quality bricks, well-laid to give a finished appearance to the face of walls.

Fair-faced brickwork: Common brickwork, roughly pointed and bagged (rubbed) over with an old sack.

Fillet: A narrow strip of wood, rectangular or triangular in section, usually fixed between the angle of two surfaces.

Firring: Building up the edges of joists, etc. with timber strips to achieve a level, sloping or higher surface when boarded.

Flange: The bottom or top surface of a steel 'I' beam or channel section.

Flashing: A lead or felt, etc. apron that covers various roof junctions.

Fletton: An extensively-used common brick, named after a village near Peterborough and made from the clay of that neighbourhood.

Floating: (see Rendering).

Flush: A flat surface, such as a flush door, or in the form of two or more components or pieces of timber being level with each other.

Gablet: The triangular end of a roof, known as a gablet when separated from a gable wall below.

Glue blocks: Short, triangular-shaped blocks, glued – and sometimes pinned – to the inside angles of steps in a wooden staircase and other constructions.

Going: The horizontal distance, in the direction of flight, of one step or of all the steps (total going) of a staircase.

Grain: The cellular structure and arrangement of fibres, etc. running lengthwise through the timber.

Green brickwork: Freshly-laid or recently-laid brickwork.

Groove: A channel shape sunk into the face or edge of timber or other material.

Grounds: Sawn or planed battens used to create a true and/or receptive fixing surface.

Gullet: The lower area of the space between saw teeth.

Gusset plate: A triangular-shaped metal joint connector.

Half-brick-thick wall: A stretcher-bond wall, measuring 100 to 115 mm thick.

Hardcore: Broken brick and hard rubble used as a substrata for concrete oversites.

Hardwood: A commercial description for the timber used in industry, which has been converted from broad-leaved, usually deciduous trees, belonging to a botanical group known as angiosperms. Occasionally, the term 'hardwood' is contradictory to the actual density and weight of a particular species; i.e. balsa wood is a hardwood which is of a lighter weight and density than most softwoods.

Heel: The back, lower portion of a saw or plane.

Hone: Sharpen.

Housing: A trench or groove usually cut across the timber.

Inner skin: The wall built on the dwelling-side of a cavity wall.
Inner string or wall string: One of the two long, deep boards that house the steps at the side of a staircase, being on the side against the wall.
In-situ concrete: Concrete units or structures cast in their actual and final location, controlled by in-situ formwork.

Jamb: The name given to the side of a door or window frame.
Joists: Structural timbers that make up the skeleton framework in timber floors, ceilings and flat roofs.

Kerf: The cut made by a saw during its progress across the material.
Knots: Roots of a tree's branches, sliced through during timber conversion. Healthy-looking knots are known as 'live' knots and those with a black ring around them are likely to fall out and are known as 'dead' knots.
Knotting: Shellac used for sealing knots (to stop them 'bleeding' or exuding resin) prior to priming. Shellac is derived from an incrustation formed by lac insects on the trees in India and nearby regions.

Lag; lagged: Wrapped or covered with boards or insulation material.
Landing nosing: The narrow, projecting board, equal in thickness and shape to the front-edge of a tread board, that is fixed on all top edges of the landing stairwell. This is often rebated on the underside to meet a reduced-thickness of floor material.
Lignum-vitae: Dark brown, black-streaked hardwood with extremely close grain. Very hard and dense; about twice the weight of British elm. Grown in the West Indies and tropical America.
Lintel: Concrete or metal beam over door or window opening.
Lugs: Projecting metal frame-cramps, as built-in fixings for metal windows.

Mitre: Usually a 45° bisection of a right-angled formation of timber (or other material) members – but the bisection of angles other than 90° is still referred to as mitring.
Muzzle velocity: Speed of nail in the barrel of a cartridge tool.

Newel posts: Plain or ornamental (turned) posts in a staircase, morticed and jointed to the outer string and handrail tenons, and attached to the floor and upper landing trimmer. The newel posts assist in creating good anchorage of the staircase at both ends, as well as providing stability to the remainder of the balustrade.
Noggings: Short, timber struts, usually between studs or joists.
Normal: The geometrical reference to a line or plane at right angles to

another; especially in the case of a line radiating from the centre of a circle, in relation to a right-angled tangent on the outside.
Nosing: The projecting front-edge of a tread board past the face of the riser, reckoned to be not more than the tread's thickness.

Open-tread stairs: Stairs without riser boards.
Outer skin: The wall built on the external side of a cavity wall.
Outer string: One of the two long, deep boards that house the steps at the open side of a staircase, away from the wall.
Oversite: An in-situ concrete slab of 100 mm minimum thickness, laid over the hardcore on the ground as part of the ground-floor structure.

Pads: Traditional wooden fixing blocks, about 100 × 75 × 9 mm, for building into bed-joints on each side of an opening. This was to facilitate the fixing of a frame after the opening was formed. The long-grain edge of the pad had to be against the fixing.
Pallets: A more traditional name for 'pads'.
p.a.r.: An abbreviation used for 'planed all round'.
Paring: Chiselling – usually across the grain.
Pellets: Cork-shaped plugs for patching counterbored holes when screwing and pelleting.
Perpends: Perpendicular cross-joints in brickwork or masonry.
Pilot hole: A small hole made with a twist drill or bradawl to take the wormed thread of a screw.
Pin or pinned: Fixed with wooden-dowel pins, but more commonly the reference is to fixing with nails or panel pins.
Pinch rod: A gauge batten for checking internal distances for parallel.
Pitch: (1) the angle of inclination to the horizontal of a roof or staircase, etc; (2) Repetitive, equal spacing of the tips or points of saw teeth or other equally spaced objects.
Plant: Equipment.
Planted mould or stop: Separate mouldings or door stops, etc. fixed by nails to the base material.
Plate: (1) A horizontal timber that holds the ends of vertical or inclined timbers in a state of alignment and framed spacing, as in the case of roofing wall-plates and stud-partitioning cill plates and head plates; (2) Metal components such as striking plates, letter plates, etc.
Plumb or plumbing: Checking or setting up work in a true, vertical position.
Plumb cut: The vertical face of an angle.
Pocket screwing: Angled or skew-screwing into shallow niches and shank holes drilled at an angle through the back-side of the timber.
Precast concrete: Concrete units cast in special mould boxes in a factory or on site, but not in their actual and final location.

Primed: Painted with priming paint after being knotted.

Profile: (1) A horizontal board attached to stakes or pegs driven into the ground, across the line of an intended foundation strip. One at each end, set clear of the digging area, has saw cuts or nails in the top edge of the board to mark the foundation and wall positions. When initially digging or building, ranging lines are set up across the boards to establish the required positions; (2) Any object or structure acting as a template in guiding the shape of something being made or built.

Quadrant: (1) A right-angled sector shape, equalling a quarter of a circle; (2) A small, wooden bead of this shape.

Rebate: A return or inverted angle removed from the edge of a piece of wood or other material.

Rendering and/or floating coats: Successive coats of coarse plaster built up to a true surface for skimming.

Resin-bonded: This is usually a reference to the cross-laminates of plywood being bonded (glued) with synthetic resins. According to the type of resin used, the plywood may be referred to as Moisture Resistant (MR), Boil Resistant (BR), or – better still – Weather and Boil Proof (WBP).

Retaining wall: A wall built to retain high-level ground on a split-level site.

Reveals: The narrow, return edges or sides of an opening in a wall.

Rise: The vertical distance of one step or of all the steps (total rise) of a staircase.

Riser: The vertical face or board of a step.

Runners: Sawn-timber beams, used in formwork, etc.

Sarking: Roof boarding and/or roofing felt.

Scribe; scribing: Techniques used in joinery or second-fixing carpentry for marking and fitting mouldings against mouldings, or straight timbers against irregular shapes or surfaces.

Seat cut: The horizontal face of an angle.

Set; setting: (1) The alternate side-bending of the tips of saw teeth; (2) The chemical setting action which brings initial hardening of glue, concrete, mortar, plaster, etc.; (3) A coat of finishing plaster (see Skimming).

Shank: The stem or shaft of a tool or screw.

Sherardized: Ironmongery (such as nails and screws) coated with zinc dust in a heated, revolving drum and achieving a penetrated coating, claimed to be more durable than galvanizing.

Shuttering: Temporary structures formed on site to contain fluid concrete until 'set' to the required shape; also known as Formwork.

Skew-nailing: Nailing at an angle of about 30° to 45° to the nailed surface, through the sides of timber, instead of through the face.

Skimming or setting coat: The fine finishing plaster, traditionally applied to ceilings and walls in a 3 to 5 mm thickness and trowelled to a smooth finish.

Soffit: The underside of a lintel, beam, ceiling, staircase, roof eaves' projection, etc.

Softwood: A commercial description for the timber used in industry, which has been converted from needle-leaved, usually coniferous 'evergreen' trees, belonging to a botanical group known as gymnosperms. Occasionally, the term 'softwood' is contradictory to the actual density and weight of a particular species; i.e. parana pine is a softwood which is quite heavy and dense, like most hardwoods.

Spall; spalling: A breaking or flaking away of the face material of concrete, brick, stone, etc.

Span: (1) *Clear span* is the horizontal distance measured between the faces of two opposite supports; (2) *Structural span*, for design calculations, is measured between half the bearing-seating on one side to half the bearing on the other; and (3) *Roof span* is measured in the direction of the ceiling joists, from the outer-edge of one wall plate to the outer-edge of the other.

Spotting: Marking a line through a slither of trowelled mortar when setting out walls and partitions on concrete foundations or oversite.

Spring or sprung: Warping, which can occur in timber after conversion and seasoning, producing a *sprung, cambered* or segmental-shaped edge adjacent to the wide face of the material. Joists and rafters should be placed with the sprung edge uppermost.

Stretcher: (1) The temporary batten at the base of a door frame or lining, that 'stretches' the legs apart until the fixing operation takes place; (2) The long face of a brick.

Strut: A timber prop, supporting a load on its end.

Stub tenon: A shortened tenon, usually morticed into its opposite member by only a half to two-thirds its potential size.

Stuck mould or rebate: Moulded shapes or rebates cut into the face of solid timber.

Studs; studding; stud partitioning: Vertical timber posts.

Tamp; tamped; tamping: A term used in concreting, referring to the level surface being zig-zagged and *tamped* (compacted) with a levelling board. The tamping is effected by bumping the board up and down as it is moved across the surface.

Tang: The pointed end of a steel tool that fits into a handle, etc.

Tangent: This is a line that lays at right angles to another line – known geometrically as a normal – that radiates from the centre of a circle.

Toe: The front of a saw, plane or boot lintel, etc.

TRADA: Timber Research and Development Association.
Tread: The horizontal face or board of a step.
Twist: (1) Warping, which can occur in timber after conversion and seasoning, producing distortion in length to a spiral-like shape; (2) Distortion in a framed-up unit caused by one or more of the members being twisted, or by ill-formed corner joints.

Voussoir: A tapered brick in a gauged brick arch.

Warp: Distortion of converted timber, caused by changing moisture content (see **Bow, Spring, Twist, Cup** and **Wind**).
Web: The connecting membrane between the flanges of a steel 'I' beam or channel section.
Wind; winding: These terms equal **Twist** and **Twisting**. The expression *in wind* means twisted and *out of wind* means not twisted.

Index